The Identifica
Weed Seedli...
Farm and Garden

R. J. CHANCELLOR, M.A.
A.R.C. Weed Research Organization
Begbroke Hill, Kidlington, Oxford

THIRD PRINTING

BLACKWELL
SCIENTIFIC PUBLICATIONS
OXFORD LONDON
EDINBURGH MELBOURNE

© 1966 Blackwell Scientific Publications
Osney Mead, Oxford OX2 0EL
8 John Street, London WC1N 2ES
9 Forrest Road, Edinburgh EH1 2QH
P.O. Box 9, North Balwyn, Victoria, Australia.

ISBN 0 632 00770 2

First published 1966
Reprinted 1972, 1978

Printed in Great Britain by
Billing & Sons Limited
Guildford, London and Worcester
and bound by
Mansell (Bookbinders) Ltd.

CONTENTS

Preface   v

Introduction   vii

Key to the Groups   1

Illustrations and notes on Weed Seedling Identification   4

Glossary   82

Bibliography   83

Index   85

PREFACE

With the rapidly expanding use of chemical weed control methods in farm and garden crops the necessity has arisen of being able to recognize weeds before they have developed out of the seedling stage. It is then that they are most easily controlled and then that the choice must often be made between several herbicides each effective against a different range of species. Correct identification is therefore a pre-requisite for success, but there are very few users of herbicides—or advisers—who are able to name seedling weeds other than the commonest kinds with any certainty.

The importance of Mr. Chancellor's book is that it provides the means by which virtually all the troublesome weeds in Britain can be readily identified as seedlings, even by those with little previous experience. It is the first comprehensive book on a subject that has long been neglected by botanists and provides a welcome expansion of the author's first book on seedling identification, which has become a standard reference work in Britain and many European countries.

In this new book 162 species of weeds are illustrated by a completely new set of drawings. For very variable species several drawings are given to illustrate the range of types. The species are classified into a number of groups to aid identification and a simple key enables the appropriate group to be selected and hence the species to be rapidly identified. Confirmation of identity is assisted by the notes on each weed, which draw attention to key characters and briefly indicate where and when each species is usually found.

This book should not only prove of assistance to farmers, growers and technical advisers, but should also be of value to students and research workers interested in studies of weed problems and populations. Gardeners, too, may find it useful.

Some readers might possibly have preferred photographs or coloured illustrations to line drawings. In fact there are few advantages in such methods of presentation. Experience has shown that the method of depicting plants used in this book is the most satisfactory for accurate identification. It is also much less expensive, a not unimportant factor in helping to ensure that this book is found in the pocket of all those who are concerned with weeds and their control.

Begbroke
May 1966

J. D. FRYER

INTRODUCTION

This book is intended as a simple guide to the identification of the seedlings of all the important weeds that are likely to be found in the British Isles. They are illustrated and compared at very young stages and to aid identification they have been arranged in 32 groups. To reach the right group quickly a key has been provided. These groups are taxonomically artificial although every effort has been made to keep closely related species together. The grouping adopted utilizes the more obvious characters of the seedlings, but as there are few useful characters and most of them are variable a few species could possibly come in more than one group. No group contains more than 12 species so once the right group is reached the naming of a seedling should be easy from the illustrations and the notes. The notes indicate the important characters for distinguishing members of the group from one another and reference is also made to similar seedlings in other groups. To help confirm the identity of seedlings information is also given on frequency, life span, habitat, distribution, soil preferences if any and periods of germination if these differ from the usual flushes of germination in spring and autumn.

The illustrations are mostly one and a half times natural size and show the seedlings from above, obliquely or from the side. Many are at the first true leaf stage with the cotyledons to right and left and the first true leaf upwards, but a number of species are shown at older stages because their later leaves differ greatly in shape from the first true leaves.

Plant names follow the second edition (1962) of *Flora of the British Isles* by A. R. Clapham, T. G. Tutin and E. F. Warburg (Cambridge University Press) with the addition of a few alternative common names. The distribution of each species has been derived from the *Atlas of the British Flora* (1962) edited by F. H. Perring and S. M. Walters (Thomas Nelson and Sons Ltd.). The few technical terms employed are explained in the glossary and a list of other publications on weed seedlings is given at the end.

The author wishes to acknowledge the very considerable help given by Miss J. M. Thurston of the Rothamsted Research Station at Harpenden and Mr. H. A. Roberts of the National Vegetable Research Station at Welles-bourne in the preparation of this book, both in providing weed seeds and seedlings and in critically examining the text and illustrations. Thanks are also due to Mrs. A. P. Chancellor and Mr. P. J. Boyle who corrected the final manuscript.

KEY TO THE GROUPS

1 The second and later true leaves divided into separate leaflets   **2**
The second true leaf not divided into leaflets   **3**

2 Cotyledons remaining below ground in the seed; the second
true leaf divided into two or four leaflets in opposite pairs   *Group 1*
Cotyledons emerging above ground; the second true leaf
divided into three leaflets   *Group 2*

3 True leaves with small, star-like, branched hairs on the upper
surface, visible only with a lens. Simple hairs may also be
present   *Group 3*
True leaves with simple hairs only or hairless   **4**

4 Cotyledons with backwardly-directed lobes at the base   *Group 4**
Cotyledons without backwardly-directed lobes at the base   **5**

5 True leaves in whorls of four or more around the stem   *Group 5*
True leaves attached singly or in opposite pairs   **6**

6 Cotyledons broader than long, asymmetrical and their stalks
long and hairy   *Group 6*
Cotyledons as long as or longer than broad   **7**

7 First true leaves very narrow and usually with several lateral
lobes or teeth   *Group 7*
First true leaves not narrow and lobed   **8**

8 First true leaves with spiny or prickly margins; cotyledons
large and fleshy   *Group 8*
First true leaves without spiny or prickly margins   **9**

9 Cotyledons with a pronounced indent at the apex, generally
kidney-shaped; seedlings large   *Group 9*
Cotyledons with a small or no indent at the apex   **10**

10 First true leaf with downwardly-directed teeth on the margins   *Group 10*
First true leaf without downwardly-directed teeth   **11**

11 True leaves with stinging hairs on the upper surface   *Group 11*
True leaves without stinging hairs   **12**

* See also Group 6

12 First true leaves with several small knobs on the margins — *Group 12*

First true leaves without small knobs on the margins — **13**

13 Cotyledons very long and narrow, at least eight times as long as broad — *Group 13**

Cotyledons narrow, between three and eight times as long as broad — **14**

Cotyledons oval or rounded, less than three times as long as broad — **17**

14 Margins of first true leaf deeply divided — *Group 14*

Margins of first true leaf shallowly toothed or lobed — *Group 15*

Margins of first true leaf entire — **15**

15 Hypocotyl long (1 cm or more) — *Group 16*

Hypocotyl short ($\frac{1}{2}$ cm or less) — **16**

16 Later true leaves deeply lobed — *Group 17*

Later true leaves entire or shallowly toothed or wavy or with a single pair of deep lobes at the base — *Group 18*

17 First true leaf or pair of leaves entire and hairless — **18**

First true leaf or pair of leaves entire and hairy or the stalks alone hairy — **19**

First true leaf or pair of leaves with wavy, toothed or lobed margins, hairy or hairless — **22**

18 Cotyledons as broad as long, tips rounded or slightly indented — *Group 19*

Cotyledons oval to long oval, tips various but not sharply pointed — *Group 20*

Cotyledons sharply pointed — *Group 21*

19 Cotyledons hairy — *Group 22*

Cotyledons glabrous — **20**

20 Cotyledons round to shortly ovoid — *Group 25*

Cotyledons oval to long oval — **21**

21 Hypocotyl long — *Group 23*

Hypocotyl short — *Group 24*

22 Leaf margins wavy in outline — *Group 26*

Leaf margins notched, toothed or lobed — **23**

23 Leaves with long woolly hairs — *Group 27*

Leaves glabrous or hairy, but not woolly — **24**

* See also Group 14

24 Cotyledons hairy   *Group 28*

   Cotyledons glabrous   **25**

25 First true leaves with deeply-lobed margins   *Group 29*

   First true leaves with toothed or shallowly-lobed margins   **26**

26 Cotyledon stalks as long as or longer than the blade   *Group 30*

   Cotyledon stalks shorter than the blade   **27**

27 Cotyledons shaped like the "spade" of playing cards; first

     true leaves in opposite pairs with margins shallowly and

     regularly notched   *Group 31*

   Cotyledons variously shaped; first true leaves with variously

     toothed margins   *Group 32*

Cotyledons remaining below ground in the seed; first true leaves of two or four leaflets in opposite pairs.

Vicia hirsuta (Hairy Tare). The first leaves always consist of two pairs of leaflets unlike the other members of this group. The relatively rounded leaflet apices also help to distinguish this species. Locally common in arable land it is found throughout most of the British Isles.

Vicia sativa (Common Vetch). The long and narrow first true leaves with their tapered points distinguish this species from the others in this group. Later leaves, however, are much shorter and broader, with a noticeable short point. Juvenile foliage is not produced if the main stem is damaged. It is an annual plant of arable and grass land throughout the British Isles.

Vicia tetrasperma (Smooth Tare). The first leaves consisting of one pair of leaflets distinguish it from *V. hirsuta*. The leaflets have less tapered points than those of the other two species. An annual arable weed, occasional in England, but less frequent in Ireland and the north of Scotland.

Lathyrus pratensis (Meadow Vetchling). The first leaves which have only one pair of leaflets separate this species from *V. hirsuta*. Minor differences in leaflet shape separate it from *V. sativa* and *V. tetrasperma*. This perennial plant is common throughout the British Isles and is frequently found in arable land after the ploughing up of permanent pasture.

Vicia hirsuta
side view × 1·5

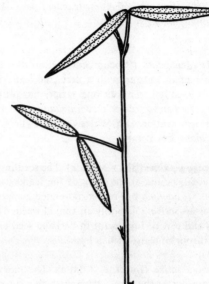

Vicia sativa
side view × 1·5

Vicia tetrasperma
oblique view × 1·5

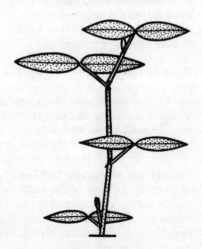

Lathyrus pratensis
side view × 1·5

The second true leaf is composed of three leaflets (one opposite pair and one terminal leaflet) while the first true leaf has either one of three leaflets; cotyledons small, oblong to oval.

Oxalis corniculata (Procumbent Yellow Sorrel). This seedling is the only member of this group with a first true leaf composed of three leaflets. The plant is usually green, but one variety has purple leaves. An annual weed of waste places and gardens, *O. corniculata* is most common in southern England, but is also scattered in Wales and elsewhere. *O. europaea* is similar to *O. corniculata*, but is rare.

Medicago lupulina (Black Medick). The seedlings of both the *Medicago* species have small points at the apex of the leaflets unlike the other plants in this group. *M. lupulina* has rather flat-ended leaflets, compared with the indented ones of *M. sativa*. Generally an annual weed, it is found frequently in turf and lawns and can be important in herbage seed crops; common in grassy situations throughout the British Isles.

Medicago sativa (Lucerne, Alfalfa). The hairy and indented leaflets which have a point at the apex, distinguish this species from all other members of this group. A perennial plant, widely grown and frequently found in arable land.

Trifolium pratense (Red Clover). The leaflets have no point at the apex unlike the *Medicago* species and it is readily distinguished from the other clovers by its large size, dull green leaves and long and conspicuous hairs. A frequently grown perennial of grassland it often occurs in arable land and is a common weed of turf.

Trifolium repens (White Clover). The absence of points at the apex of the leaflets separates this plant from the *Medicago* species. It is hairless, unlike Red Clover, and the apex of the terminal leaflet differs from that of *T. dubium*. It often has white marks near the base of the leaflets (see illustration). Common throughout the British Isles in grassland where it is often sown, and frequently a weed of turf. The seed germinates mainly in late spring.

Trifolium dubium (Yellow Suckling Clover, Lesser Hop Trefoil). The absence of points at the apex of the leaflets separates this plant from the *Medicago* species and the heart-shaped terminal leaflet of the second true leaf separates it from the other *Trifolium* species. *T. dubium* is an annual weed of grassland, gateways and waste places throughout the British Isles. It occurs frequently in turf and occasionally in herbage seed crops. Germination takes place mainly in the spring.

Oxalis corniculata
top view × 1·5

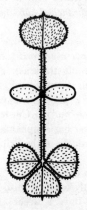

Medicago lupulina
top view × 1·5

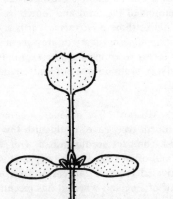

Medicago sativa
top view × 1·5

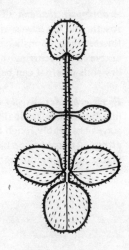

Trifolium pratense
top view × 1·5

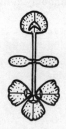

Trifolium repens
top view × 1·5

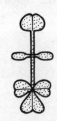

Trifolium dubium
top view × 1·5

GROUP 3

First true leaves with very small star-like hairs (visible only with a hand-lens). Simple unbranched hairs may also be present.

Capsella bursa-pastoris (Shepherd's Purse). Later leaves are very variable in shape (see illustrations). The margins of the third and fourth true leaves are entire even in cut-leaved forms unlike those of *Erysimum*. It is a larger plant than *Arabidopsis*. The leaves of *Capsella* are silvery or grey-green and may be tinged with purple. Cut-leaved forms resemble *Papaver rhoeas* (Group 17), but *Papaver* has simple hairs only. A common weed of arable land and waste places throughout the British Isles.

Erysimum cheiranthoides (Treacle Mustard). The broader, squarer cotyledons and slightly toothed third and fourth true leaves distinguish this plant from *Capsella*. It is a larger and less compact seedling than *Arabidopsis*. Like *Capsella* the leaves are greyish and often tinged with purple. It is an annual or over-wintering weed of cultivated ground, gardens and waste places. It occurs mainly in the eastern half of England where it has recently increased in frequency.

Arabidopsis thaliana (Thale Cress, Wall Cress). The compact dark-green rosette and the leaves with large branched hairs visible to the naked eye make this seedling unmistakeable. A small annual or sometimes biennial weed of arable land occurring throughout the British Isles. It is often associated with dry soils where it can be abundant.

Picris echioides (Bristly Ox-tongue). Both leaves and cotyledons of this seedling taper very gradually into broad stalks. The bristly hairs make the true leaves noticeably rough to the touch unlike those of the other members of this group. An annual or biennial weed of roadsides, field headlands and waste places occurring throughout England and Wales, most commonly in the east.

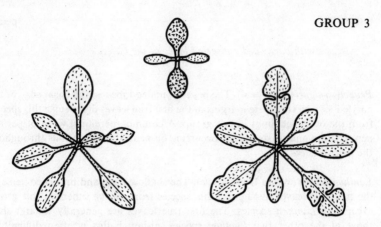

Capsella bursa-pastoris
top view ×1·5

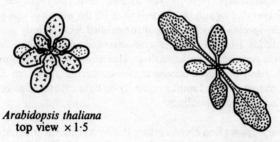

Arabidopsis thaliana
top view ×1·5

Erysimum cheiranthoides
top view ×1·5

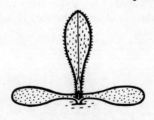

Picris echioides
oblique view ×1·5
hairs on leaf margin

Cotyledons with backwardly directed lobes at the base.

Prunella vulgaris (Self-heal). The broad rounded lobes on the basal edge of the cotyledons and the entire margins of the first true leaves distinguish this species from the other seedlings in this group. A common perennial weed of permanent pasture and waste places, occurring on neutral or basic soils throughout the British Isles.

Lamium album (White Dead-nettle). The shallow teeth and branched veins of the first true leaves distinguish this species from all the others in this group except the *Lamium* species. The first true leaves are generally squarer than those of the other two *Lamium* species, although this is often difficult to determine. A perennial weed of waste ground, gardens and roadsides throughout the British Isles, but most common in England.

Lamium amplexicaule (Henbit). The shallow teeth and branched veins of the first true leaves distinguish this species from all the others in this group except the *Lamium* species, which can be distinguished from it only with difficulty: *L. album* tends to have squarer true leaves than *L. amplexicaule* and *L. purpureum* is generally a darker colour. Henbit can be found in most parts of the British Isles, but most commonly in southern and eastern England. An annual weed that is found most frequently on light cultivated soils and is often a weed of horticultural holdings.

Lamium purpureum (Red Dead-nettle). It differs from the other species in this group, except for the other *Lamium* species, in having shallow teeth and branched veins on the true leaves. *L. album* has squarer leaves and *L. amplexicaule* is a lighter colour, but they are difficult to separate. An annual weed that is widespread on waste land and cultivated ground, especially gardens, throughout the British Isles.

Prunella vulgaris
top view × 1·5

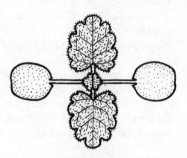

Lamium album
top view × 1·5

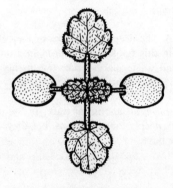

Lamium amplexicaule
top view × 1·5

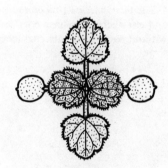

Lamium purpureum
top view × 1·5

Galeopsis tetrahit (Common Hemp-nettle, Day Nettle). *G. tetrahit* is indistinguishable from *G. speciosa* without flowers, but the regular teeth and veining of the first leaves distinguish it from all the other seedlings in this group. A common annual weed of arable land throughout the British Isles.

Galeopsis speciosa (Large-flowered Hemp-nettle). *G. speciosa* is indistinguishable from *G. tetrahit* without flowers, although easily separated from the other species in this group by the regular teeth and veining of the first true leaves. Frequently associated with black peaty soils, it is widespread in the British Isles although less common than *G. tetrahit*.

Erodium cicutarium (Common Storksbill). The deep lateral lobes of the cotyledons are unique amongst the species in this book.* *Erodium* is an annual weed of cultivated ground, grassland and waste places occurring mainly in southern and eastern England and on sandy soils around the coastline.

* *Lepidium sativum* (uncommon) and *Amsinkia intermedia* (rare, in Suffolk and elsewhere) also have cotyledons with deeply lobed margins, but they are without backwardly-directed lobes at the base.

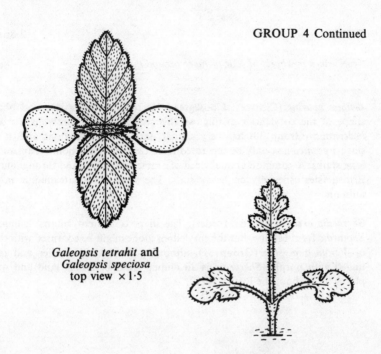

Galeopsis tetrahit and
Galeopsis speciosa
top view × 1·5

Erodium cicutarium
oblique view × 1·5

True leaves in whorls of four or more around the stem.

Galium aparine (Cleavers, Goosegrass, Herrif). The large size and oblong shape of the cotyledons distinguish this seedling from *Sherardia*. *Veronica hederifolia* (Group 30) has very similar dark-green cotyledons and at this stage *Veronica* can only be separated from *Galium* by the pointed apices and long stalks. A common annual weed of arable and waste land throughout the British Isles especially on heavy soils. The seeds germinate mainly in late autumn.

Sherardia arvensis (Field Madder). The shape of the cotyledons distinguish *Sherardia* from *Galium*, but the cotyledons alone might be confused with those of *Veronica persica* (Group 31), although *Veronica* is smaller and often tinged with purple. *Sherardia* is an annual weed of arable land and waste places throughout the British Isles.

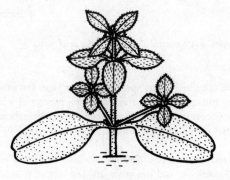

Galium aparine
oblique view × 1·5

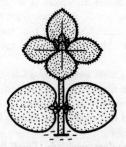

Sherardia arvensis
oblique view × 1·5

GROUP 6

4 Species

Cotyledons broader than long and asymmetrical; stalks long and hairy.

Geranium pratense (Meadow Cranesbill). This species is larger than the other three Cranesbills and the first true leaf is more divided. It is a perennial weed of damp grassland and occurs occasionally in herbage seed crops. Widespread throughout the British Isles, but only locally common.

Geranium dissectum (Cut-leaved Cranesbill). The less divided first true leaf separates *G. dissectum* from *G. pratense* and the more divided second true leaf distinguishes it from the other two *Geranium* species. A common annual weed of arable land, grassland and waste places throughout the British Isles.

Geranium molle (Dove's-foot Cranesbill). The second true leaf is less divided than that of *G. pratense* and *G. dissectum*, but it cannot be distinguished from *G. pusillum* as a seedling. A common annual weed of arable, grass and waste land throughout the British Isles.

Geranium pusillum (Small-flowered Cranesbill). It cannot be distinguished from *G. molle* as a seedling, but the less divided second true leaf distinguishes it from the other two species. It occupies similar habitats to *G. molle*, but is less important and less widespread.

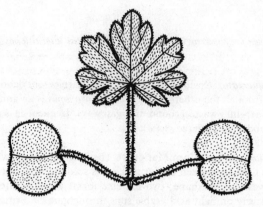

Geranium pratense
top view ×1·5

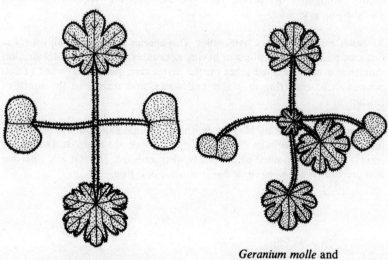

Geranium dissectum
top view ×1·5

Geranium molle and
Geranium pusillum
top view ×1·5 ' .

First true leaves very narrow and usually with several lateral lobes or teeth.

Coronopus squamatus (Swine-cress). The long narrow cotyledons separate this seedling from all the others in the group. *Coronopus* is an annual weed of arable land margins, waste ground and gateways, frequent in southern and eastern England, but scattered elsewhere.

Chrysanthemum segetum (Corn Marigold). The long hypocotyl, waxy appearance and the light blue-green colour make this seedling very distinctive. The first true leaves vary in shape; two extreme forms are illustrated. It grows almost exclusively on light acid arable soils throughout the British Isles.

Achillea millefolium (Yarrow, Milfoil). The hairy true leaves with their sharply pointed lateral lobes or teeth distinguish this seedling from the others in this group. Yarrow is a perennial plant and occasionally a problem in lawns. It occurs throughout the British Isles and seedlings are frequently found in ploughed-up grassland.

Anthemis arvensis (Corn Chamomile). This species differs from all others in this group except for *Achillea* in having noticeably hairy leaves. *Achillea* has shorter and more pointed lobes on the first leaves. An annual weed of calcareous soils, occurring in arable and waste land mainly in the south of England.

Anthemis cotula (Stinking Mayweed). This seedling is hairy but less noticeably than *A. arvensis*, the hairs often occurring only on the under-surface of the leaves. Older plants smell unpleasantly when crushed. Habitat and distribution are similar to *A. arvensis*, but it is more common.

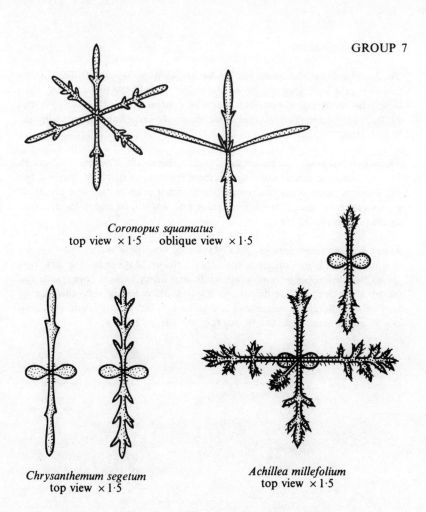

Coronopus squamatus
top view × 1·5   oblique view × 1·5

Chrysanthemum segetum
top view × 1·5

Achillea millefolium
top view × 1·5

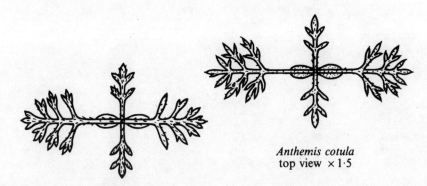

Anthemis cotula
top view × 1·5

Anthemis arvensis
top view × 1·5

GROUP 7 Continued

Tripleurospermum maritimum ssp. inodorum (Scentless Mayweed). This species tends to have a shorter and broader terminal lobe to the first true leaf than other species in this group, but it can be confused with the *Anthemis* and *Matricaria* species. This is one of the most important arable weeds in the British Isles.

Matricaria recutita (=*chamomilla*) (Wild Chamomile, Scented Mayweed). This species is difficult to distinguish from the other hairless Mayweeds, but *Tripleurospermum* often has a broader terminal lobe to the first leaves. It grows generally on lighter soils in arable and waste land and is locally common in England and Wales.

Matricaria matricarioides (Rayless Mayweed, Pineapple Weed). This species is difficult to distinguish from the other hairless Mayweeds. The first true leaves have few lobes or none at all, while later on their shiny appearance and broad stalks help in identification. Rayless Mayweed is very common in horticultural holdings, waste land and gateways, but is only found occasionally in arable land. It occurs throughout the British Isles.

Tripleurospermum maritimum
ssp. inodorum
top view × 1·5

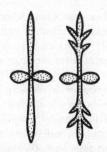

Matricaria matricarioides
and *Matrica recutita*
top view × 1·5

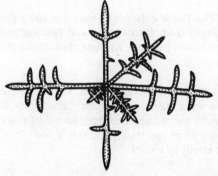

Matricaria recutita
top view × 1·5

Matricaria matricarioides
top view × 1·5

First true leaves with spiny or prickly margins, cotyledons large and fleshy.

Onopordum acanthium (Scotch Thistle, Cotton Thistle). The large angular leaves covered with white cottony hairs distinguish this species from the other thistles. It occurs throughout England and Wales in grassland and waste places, but is never very common.

Cirsium eriophorum (Woolly Thistle). The small prickles on the leaf margins and the relatively long-stalked first leaves are the only distinguishing characters of this thistle. Very similar to *Carduus acanthoides* and apparently differing only in leaf venation. It is found in grassland and on roadsides, on calcareous soils only, throughout England and Wales.

Cirsium palustre (Marsh Thistle). This thistle differs from the other species in having longer spines on the margins of the first true leaves and broader, less tapered leaf bases. A biennial weed of wet pastures, common throughout the British Isles.

Cirsium arvense (Creeping Thistle). This species has fewer spines on the margins of the first leaves than the other thistles. One of the worst weeds, it occurs abundantly in grassland, arable and waste land throughout the British Isles. It spreads by far-creeping roots which can readily regenerate new plants from small pieces, and to a lesser extent by seed.

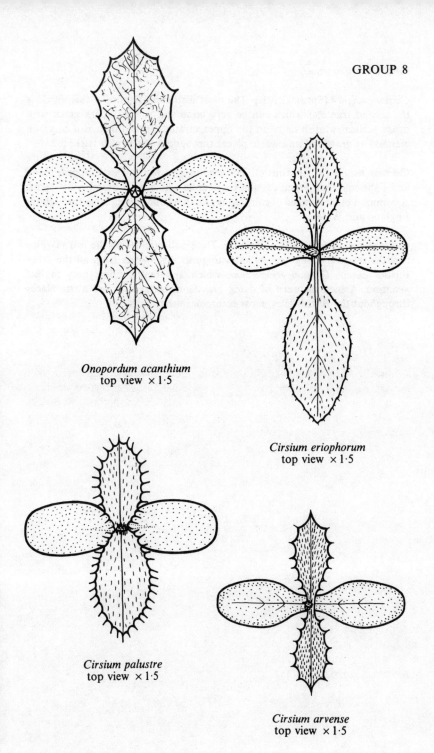

Onopordum acanthium
top view × 1·5

Cirsium eriophorum
top view × 1·5

Cirsium palustre
top view × 1·5

Cirsium arvense
top view × 1·5

Cirsium vulgare (Spear Thistle). The most distinctive feature of this thistle is the second true leaf which can be very large and is a dull dark green with dense vertical whitish hairs on the upper surface. Spear thistle is a common biennial of grassland and waste places throughout the British Isles.

Carduus nutans (Musk Thistle). The seedlings of Musk Thistle appear shiny and light-coloured, especially the cotyledons which have broad white veins. A common biennial weed of calcareous grassland and waste places throughout England and Wales.

Carduus acanthoides (Welted Thistle). The small prickles on the leaf margins and the relatively long leaf stalks distinguish this species from all the other thistles except *Cirsium eriophorum*, which apparently differs only in leaf venation. A biennial weed of damp grassland, hedgerows and waste places throughout the British Isles, most common in the south.

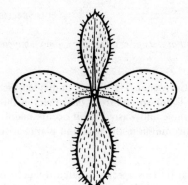

Cirsium vulgare
top view × 1·5

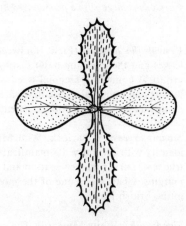

Carduus nutans
top view × 1·5

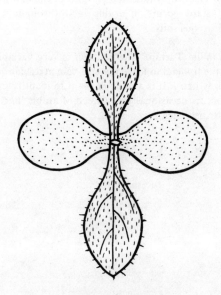

Carduus acanthoides
top view × 1·5

Cotyledons large with a pronounced indent at the apex; generally kidney-shaped.

Convolvulus arvensis (Field Bindweed, Cornbine). The simple undivided first leaves and the climbing habit distinguish this species from the others in this group. A common perennial weed of arable and waste land it occurs mainly in England and Wales. Seedlings are uncommon in the field and plants arise mainly as shoots from root fragments.

Sinapis arvensis (Charlock, Wild Mustard). This species is often difficult to identify with certainty. Its main features are: a broad rounded tip to the first true leaf, fairly regular venation and relatively shallow indentation of the leaf margins. Charlock is one of the most common annual weeds of arable land in the British Isles.

Sinapis alba (White Mustard). The deeply indented margins of the first leaves are characteristic. White Mustard occurs in arable land throughout the British Isles, especially on calcareous soils.

Brassica rapa ssp. campestris (Wild Turnip). The first leaf is very variable in shape. The lateral veins near the tip tend to leave the mid-vein at a wide angle and the leaf is generally sparsely hairy. It is a difficult plant to identify in the seedling stage. Wild Turnip occurs occasionally as a weed of arable land and waste places throughout the British Isles.

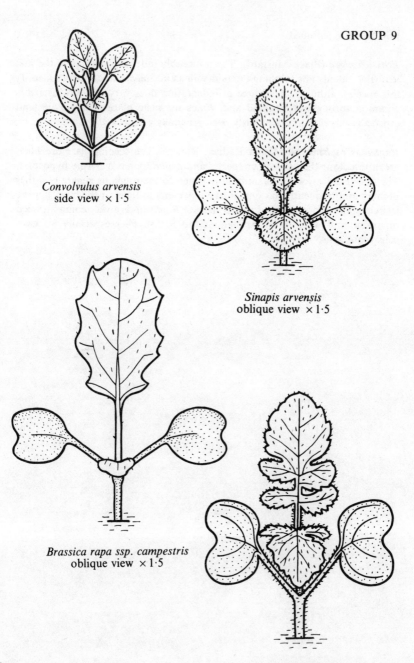

Convolvulus arvensis
side view × 1·5

Sinapis arvensis
oblique view × 1·5

Brassica rapa ssp. campestris
oblique view × 1·5

Sinapis alba
oblique view × 1·5

Brassica nigra (Black Mustard). The noticeably indented margins of the first leaf (the indents not reaching the mid-vein as in *Sinapis alba*) help to identify this species, although the degree of indentation does vary. Black Mustard is common throughout England and Wales in waste places and arable land especially where it has previously been grown as a crop.

Raphanus raphanistrum (Wild Radish, Runch). The seedling is more blue-green in colour than the other species and generally has a purple hypocotyl. The first true leaf, which is noticeably rough to the touch, is generally rather pointed and frequently has one or two independent lobes at the base, but the last character is not confined to this species. *Raphanus* is a very common weed of arable and waste land throughout the British Isles especially on non-calcareous soils.

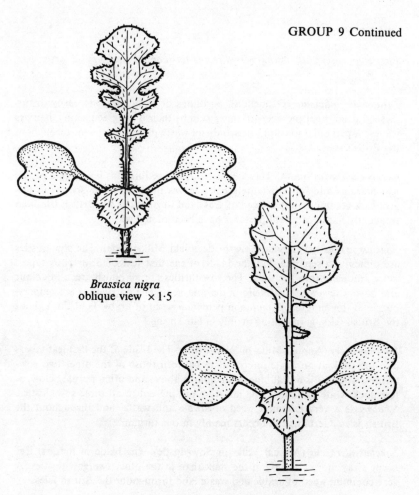

Brassica nigra
oblique view × 1·5

Raphanus raphanistrum
oblique view × 1·5

First true leaves with downwardly directed teeth on the margins.

Taraxacum officinale (Dandelion). Seedlings of Dandelion are easily distinguished from other members of this group by their dark-green, shiny, hairless leaves. A perennial weed of grassland and waste places, abundant throughout the British Isles.

Crepis capillaris (Smooth Hawk's-beard). This seedling has fewer teeth on the leaf margins and more definitely hairy leaves than the other species in this group. A common annual weed of grassland throughout the British Isles and frequently found after old pastures have been ploughed.

Sonchus arvensis (Perennial Sow-thistle, Field Milk-thistle). The sow-thistles are difficult to separate, but the blade of the first leaf of *S. arvensis* tapers more gradually into the stalk. The sow-thistles are all bluish-green in colour and have a few white hairs along the mid-vein. The cotyledons are reddish-purple at the margins. A common perennial weed of arable land throughout the British Isles, germinating mainly in late spring.

Sonchus asper (Annual Milk- or Sow-thistle). The blade of the first leaf tapers into the stalk at an angle intermediate between those of the other two sow-thistles. The leaf is a dull blue-green colour above and often purple below. A few thick white hairs near the mid-vein are present in all three sow-thistles. *S. asper* is a very common weed of arable and waste land throughout the British Isles. Germination occurs mainly in the autumn.

Sonchus oleraceus (Annual Milk- or Sow-thistle). The blade of the first leaf is cut away more abruptly at the stalk than in the other two sow-thistles. A very common weed of arable and waste land throughout the British Isles.

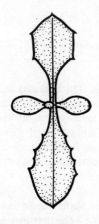

Taraxacum officinale
top view × 1·5

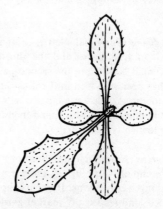

Crepis capillaris
top view × 1·5

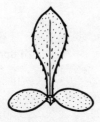

Sonchus arvensis
oblique view × 1·5

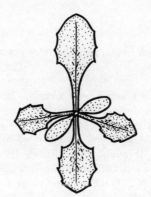

Sonchus asper
top view × 1·5   oblique view × 1·5

Sonchus oleraceus
oblique view × 1·5

GROUP 11

True leaves with stinging hairs on the upper surface.

Urtica dioica (Perennial Nettle, Stinging Nettle). The rounded apex of the first pair of true leaves and the shorter cotyledons distinguish this species from Annual Nettle, but the second pair of true leaves (the right-hand one of which has been removed in the illustration), resemble those of Annual Nettle quite closely. A weed principally of waste places, especially on fertile soils around buildings, it is also found in grassland and occurs commonly throughout the British Isles.

Urtica urens (Annual Nettle). Seedlings of Annual Nettle can be distinguished from Perennial Nettle by the more pointed teeth on the first true leaves and by the longer cotyledons. It occurs throughout the British Isles as a weed of cultivated land (especially market gardens) and waste places, particularly on light soils.

GROUP 12

First true leaves with several small knobs on the margins.

Epilobium hirsutum (Codlins and Cream, Great Hairy Willow-herb). The hairless cotyledons distinguish this plant from the *Kickxia* species and the rounded shape of the first true leaves from *Mycelis*. Later leaves of *Epilobium* are variably hairy. A perennial weed of ditch-banks and other damp places it occurs commonly throughout the British Isles with the exception of the extreme north. The seeds are wind dispersed and the seedlings may therefore be found at a distance from the parent plant.

Mycelis muralis (Wall Lettuce). The triangular first true leaf with the marginal knobs often tinged with purple is very distinctive. An unimportant weed of garden paths, walls and waste places it occurs mainly in England and Wales.

Kickxia elatine (Sharp-leaved Fluellen). The hairy cotyledons distinguish this species from *Epilobium* and *Mycelis* and it differs from *K. spuria* in its larger, more triangular cotyledons and bluntly-pointed true leaves. An infrequent weed of arable land on light soils mostly in southern and eastern England. Germination takes place mainly in the spring.

Urtica dioica
top view × 1·5

Urtica urens
top view × 1·5

Epilobium hirsutum
top view × 1·5

Mycelis muralis
oblique view × 1·5

Kickxia elatine
top view × 1·5

Kickxia spuria
top view × 1·5

Kickxia spuria (Round-leaved Fluellen). The hairy cotyledons separate this species from *Epilobium* and *Mycelis* and it differs from *K. elatine* in having small rounded cotyledons and less pointed first true leaves. Similar in distribution, habitats and germination to *K. elatine*.

Cotyledons very long and narrow, at least eight times as long as broad.

Fumaria officinalis (Fumitory). The cotyledons and leaves of Fumitory are a distinctive light blue-green colour and the hypocotyl is long and pinkish. The only other seedling in this group with a divided first true leaf is *Scandix*, which has a more finely divided leaf with smaller segments. *Fumaria* is a common weed of arable land and waste places throughout the British Isles. Seedlings appear mainly in spring, but in some years there is a flush of germination in late autumn also. There are several other more local species of *Fumaria* that resemble *F. officinalis* in the seedling stage.

Scandix pecten-veneris (Shepherd's Needle, Venus's Comb). The only other species in this group with a divided first true leaf is *Fumaria*, which has a less divided leaf and is a distinctive light blue-green colour. *Scandix* is a weed of arable land particularly on calcareous soils in eastern and southern England. It germinates mainly in early spring.

Papaver argemone (Prickly Long-headed Poppy). Although the first pair of true leaves are entire, the third and later leaves are lobed, unlike all the other species in this group excepting *Scandix* and *Fumaria* which have finely divided leaves. In small seedlings the cotyledons lie flat on the soil, a feature characteristic of all poppies (see Group 17), with their tips often turned to one side. This species is common on light arable soils in the south and east of England, but has a scattered distribution elsewhere.

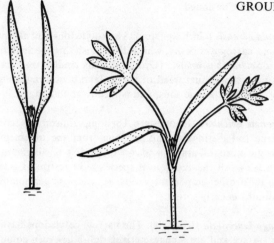

Fumaria officinalis
side view ×1·5   oblique view ×1·5

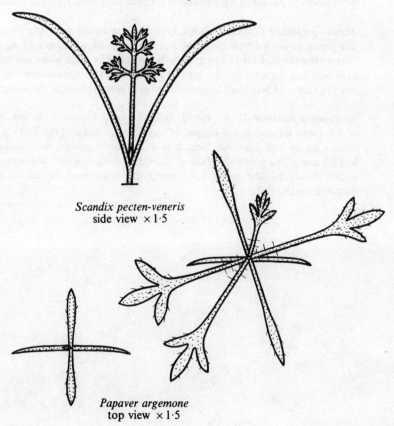

Scandix pecten-veneris
side view ×1·5

Papaver argemone
top view ×1·5

GROUP 13 Continued

Spergula arvensis (Corn Spurrey). The cotyledons and all true leaves are very long and narrow yet fleshy, which distinguish this species from the rest of this group. *Scleranthus annuus* (Group 18) has similar true leaves, but broader cotyledons. An annual weed of arable land it occurs throughout the British Isles except on alkaline soils, and is locally abundant.

Polygonum aviculare (Knotgrass). The long crimson hypocotyl and the broad first true leaf distinguish this seedling from the others in this group. An important weed of arable and waste land it is abundant throughout the British Isles. All the *Polygonum* species have restricted germination periods unlike most other important weeds. *P. aviculare* germinates for only about two months in early spring.

Plantago lanceolata (Ribwort). The narrow cotyledons have a groove on the upper surface and are a characteristic dull blue-green colour. This perennial weed of grassland is common throughout the British Isles and seedlings are often found in ploughed-up pasture. It germinates in both spring and autumn.

Montia perfoliata (Spring Beauty). This seedling differs from the others in this group in having true leaves with a definite stalk which is as long as or longer than the leaf blade and gracefully curved. The plant is associated with light soils and is a serious nuisance in a few nurseries. It is occasional throughout England and Scotland. Germination takes place mainly in the autumn.

Tragopogon pratensis (Goat's Beard, Jack-go-to-bed-at-noon). The cotyledons of this plant are among the longest of any British weed and the first true leaf is also longer and narrower than that of any other species with undivided leaf-blades in this group. A plant of grassland, roadsides and waste places it occurs throughout the British Isles, commonly in England, but less so in the west and north.

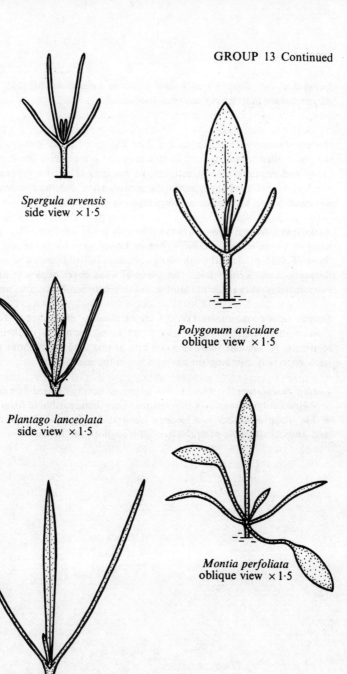

Spergula arvensis
side view × 1·5

Polygonum aviculare
oblique view × 1·5

Plantago lanceolata
side view × 1·5

Montia perfoliata
oblique view × 1·5

Tragopogon pratensis
side view × 0·75

GROUP 14 4 Species

Cotyledons between three and eight times as long as broad; first true leaves deeply divided (half way to the middle or more).

Aethusa cynapium (Fool's Parsley). The first true leaf of *Aethusa* is the least deeply divided of any species in this group. All the leaves are hairless, dark green and concave with slightly raised margins. This is a common annual weed of arable land throughout the British Isles, but least common in the west and north. Germination takes place in spring only.

Anthriscus sylvestris (Cow Parsley). The only other seedling in this group with hairy first true leaves is *Daucus*, but its leaves have narrower segments than those of *Anthriscus*. Although often abundant in hedgerows and waste places throughout the British Isles, this biennial weed never occurs in arable land. Germination takes place in suitable weather between November and April.

Daucus carota ssp. carota (Wild Carrot). *Daucus* differs from *Aethusa* and *Conium* in having hairy true leaves and from *Anthriscus* in their narrower segments. A biennial weed of grass and arable land throughout the British Isles, especially common on chalky soils in the south-east.

Conium maculatum (Hemlock). The large and deeply divided first leaf and the net-veined cotyledons make this species easily distinguishable from the others in this group. Hemlock is a biennial weed of damp places, hedgerows, grassland and occasionally of arable land, throughout the British Isles.

Page 38.

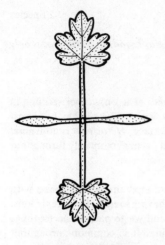

Aethusa cynapium
top view × 1·5

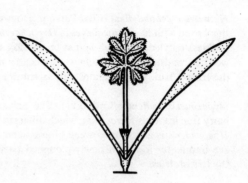

Anthriscus sylvestris
side view × 1·5

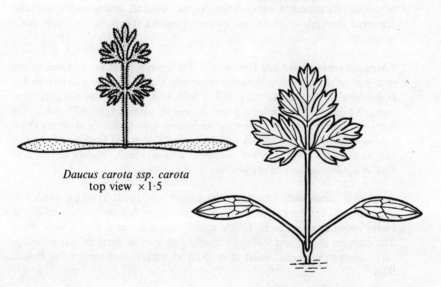

Daucus carota ssp. carota
top view × 1·5

Conium maculatum
oblique view × 1·5

Cotyledons between three and eight times as long as broad; first true leaves only shallowly lobed or toothed.

Heracleum sphondylium (Cow Parsnip, Hogweed). The only other seedling in this group with hairy true leaves is *Hypochaeris*, which differs in having almost stalkless cotyledons which lie flat on the soil surface. *Heracleum* is a biennial weed of roadsides, hedges and waste places and occurs commonly throughout the British Isles. It germinates only in spring.

Hypochaeris radicata (Cat's Ear). The only other plant in this group with hairy true leaves is *Heracleum*, which differs in having long-stalked cotyledons. *Hypochaeris* is a perennial weed of grassland and waste places; the seedlings are frequently found in newly-ploughed pasture. It is common throughout the British Isles.

Chenopodium hybridum (Sowbane). The long hypocotyl and slight mealiness of the true leaves (best seen on the leaf-bud) distinguish this seedling from the others in this group. An uncommon annual weed of arable and waste land scattered through southern and eastern England. Germination takes place in spring.

Chenopodium rubrum (Red Goosefoot). The curved lobes at the bases of the first pair of leaves are a very characteristic shape. (In the illustration the right-hand leaf of the second pair has been removed to show the cotyledon beneath.) The leaves are light green in colour, often tinged with red at the margins, and shiny. The lobing varies in later leaves, the third leaves often having three pairs. An annual weed of waste places and farmyards where it can be abundant, but it is less common in arable land. Mainly confined to England. Germination takes place in spring.

Leontodon autumnalis (Autumn Hawkweed or Hawkbit). This species is characterized by the cotyledons, which lie flat on the soil surface (the true leaves growing more erect) and are usually not in direct line with each other. The margins of the first leaf are variable and may be more or less entire. A very common perennial weed of permanent pasture throughout the British Isles.

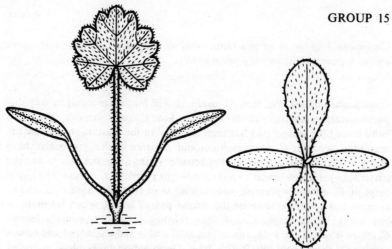

Heracleum sphondylium
oblique view ×1·5

Hypochaeris radicata
top view ×1·5

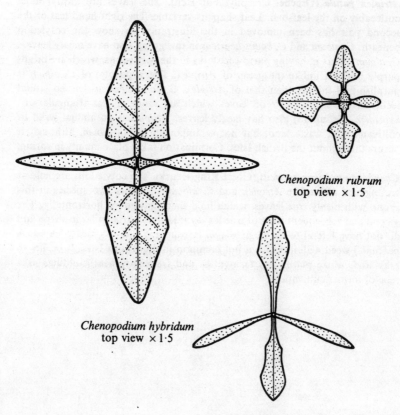

Chenopodium rubrum
top view ×1·5

Chenopodium hybridum
top view ×1·5

Leontodon autumnalis
top view ×1·5

41

Cotyledons between three and eight times as long as broad; first true leaves entire; hypocotyl long (about 1 cm or more).

Chenopodium album (Fat Hen, Goosefoot). The leaves are mealy, a very distinctive feature especially of the leaf-bud. Leaf shape is variable. The right-hand leaf of the second pair has been removed in the illustration to show the cotyledon beneath. *C. bonus-henricus* and *Atriplex* in this group also have mealy leaves: *Atriplex*, however, has broader stalks to the cotyledons and the cotyledons are green beneath unlike the bright purple of *C. album*. The hypocotyl of *C. album* is purplish and thinner than that of *Atriplex*. *C. bonus-henricus* has no lateral teeth on the second pair of leaves, which are more or less triangular in shape. *C. hybridum* (Group 15) also has mealy leaves. *C. album* is one of the worst annual weeds of arable and waste land and occurs commonly throughout the British Isles. Germination takes place in spring and summer.

Atriplex patula (Orache, Creeping Fat Hen). The leaves are mealy, most noticeably on the leaf-bud. Leaf shape is variable. The right-hand leaf of the second pair has been removed in the illustration to show the cotyledon beneath. *C. album* and *C. bonus-henricus* in this group also have mealy leaves: *C. album* differs in having narrower stalks to the cotyledons, which are bright purple beneath unlike the green of *Atriplex*. The hypocotyl of *C. album* is purplish and thinner than that of *Atriplex*. *C. bonus-henricus* has no lateral teeth on the second pair of leaves which are more or less triangular. *C. hybridum* (Group 15) also has mealy leaves. *Atriplex* is an annual weed of cultivated and waste land, but not so important as *C. album*, although it occurs throughout the British Isles. Germination takes place mainly in spring.

Chenopodium bonus-henricus (Good King Henry). The cotyledons are held at an angle of 45° unlike *Atriplex* and *C. album*, the other two species in this group with mealy true leaves, which hold their cotyledons horizontally. The second and subsequent pairs of true leaves are broadly triangular in shape and do not have lateral teeth. *C. hybridum* (Group 15) also has mealy leaves. A perennial weed widespread but not common in the British Isles. It occurs in grassland, waste places and farmyards, and frequently near buildings as a relic of former cultivation.

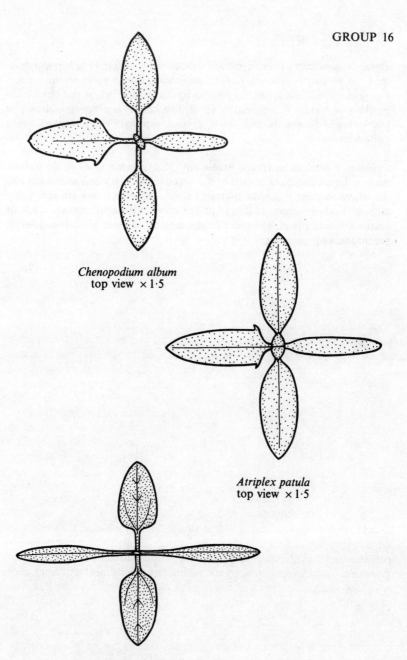

Chenopodium album
top view × 1·5

Atriplex patula
top view × 1·5

Chenopodium bonus-henricus
top view × 1·5

Datura stramonium (Thorn-apple). This species has a very long hypocotyl, up to 3 cm in length. The only other non-mealy leaved plant in this group, *Polygonum convolvulus*, has less pointed tips to the cotyledons and basal lobes on the true leaves. Widespread in the British Isles it appears sporadically in arable land, farmyards and waste ground especially in hot years. Very poisonous.

Polygonum convolvulus (Black Bindweed). The rounded lobes at the base of the true leaves are characteristic of this species. The hypocotyl is crimson and the whole seedling is a reddish-green colour. The true leaves are very shiny especially when young. It is one of the more important annual weeds of arable and waste land, and occurs commonly throughout the British Isles. It germinates only in spring.

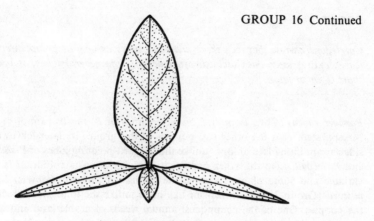

Datura stramonium
top view × 1·5

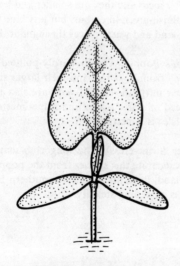

Polygonum convolvulus
oblique view × 1·5

Cotyledons narrow, between three and eight times as long as broad; first true leaves entire, later ones divided, often deeply, into several lobes; hypocotyl short ($\frac{1}{2}$ cm or less).

Papaver rhoeas (Corn Poppy). Young seedlings of *P. rhoeas* cannot readily be separated from the other two poppies in this group. Its later leaves have sideways-pointing lateral lobes unlike the forward-pointing lobes of *P. dubium* and *P. lecoqii*. Like the other poppies it is bluish-green in colour. It is very variable and some plants resemble the cut-leaved form of *Capsella bursa-pastoris* (Group 3), which has star-like hairs unlike the long simple hairs of the poppies. One of the commonest annual weeds of arable land and waste places, it occurs throughout the British Isles although more rarely in the west and north.

Papaver dubium (Long-headed Poppy). The lateral lobes of later leaves are forwardly directed unlike *P. rhoeas* and they are smaller and less pointed than *P. lecoqii*. The seedling is bluish-green in colour, but less blue than *P. rhoeas*. A common weed of arable land and waste places throughout the British Isles.

Papaver lecoqii (Babington's Poppy). The forwardly-pointed lobes of later leaves distinguish this poppy from *P. rhoeas* and their larger size and sharper points from *P. dubium*. Their purplish-red mid-veins are also a distinguishing feature. An uncommon weed of waste places and sometimes of arable land; distribution in the British Isles is uncertain.

Coronopus didymus (Lesser Swine-cress). The long club-shaped cotyledons and the hairless true leaves separate this species from the poppies. An annual weed of arable and waste land, it occurs mainly in southern England, Wales and southern Ireland, but is spreading steadily.

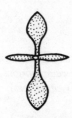

Papaver rhoeas, Papaver dubium
and *Papaver lecoqii*
top view × 1·5

Papaver rhoeas
top view × 1·5

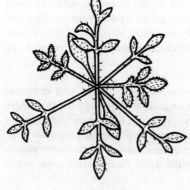

Papaver rhoeas
top view × 1·5

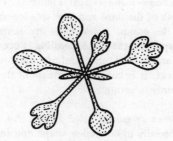

Papaver dubium
top view × 1·5

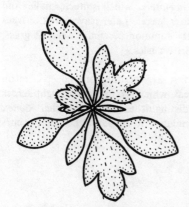

Papaver lecoqii
top view × 1·5

Coronopus didymus
top view × 1·5

Cotyledons narrow, between three and eight times as long as broad; first leaves entire, later ones entire or shallowly toothed or with wavy margins, or with a single pair of deep lobes at the base; hypocotyl short ($\frac{1}{2}$ cm or less).

Gnaphalium uliginosum (Marsh Cudweed). The dense white woolly hairs on the true leaves distinguish this species from the others in this group; a common annual weed of acid sandy soils in damp arable land and waste places throughout the British Isles. Germination takes place mainly in spring.

Scleranthus annuus (Annual Knawel). The long narrow true leaves are very distinctive. *Spergula arvensis* (Group 13) has similar leaves but differs in being a lighter green and having narrower cotyledons. An annual weed of cultivated ground and waste places it occurs on dry and especially on acid sandy soils throughout the British Isles except for the extreme north. Germination takes place in spring.

Plantago major (Great Plantain). The characteristic veining and marginal teeth of the third and later true leaves distinguish this species from the others in the group. A few hairs are normally present. The hypocotyl is usually purple and the whole seedling is occasionally deep purple. A perennial weed of arable land, grassland and open waste ground, especially in gateways and tracks, it is common throughout the British Isles. Germination takes place mainly in spring.

Rumex crispus (Curled Dock). All the species of *Rumex* are very similar especially in cotyledon shape and in colour. The leaves are often tinged or spotted with crimson (see illustration). *R. crispus* has a more pointed leaf than the other *Rumex* species, except *R. acetosella*, which is much smaller and has a pair of lobes at the base of the later leaves. Later leaves of *R. crispus* have crisped undulating margins. A very common perennial weed of grass, arable and waste land throughout the British Isles.

Rumex obtusifolius (Broad-leaved Dock). A large seedling often deep crimson in colour. The bottom of the first true leaf, which is either cut straight across or has slight downward-directed lobes, distinguishes it from the other *Rumex* species. Distribution and habitats are similar to *R. crispus*, although it occurs less frequently in arable land.

Gnaphalium uliginosum
top view × 1·5

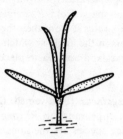

Scleranthus annuus
oblique view × 1·5

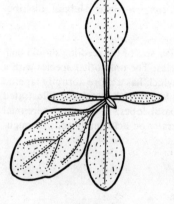

Plantago major
top view × 1·5

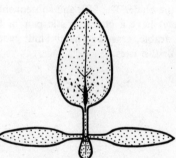

Rumex crispus
top view × 1·5

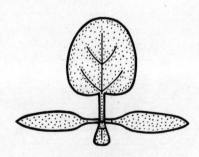

Rumex obtusifolius
top view × 1·5

Rumex conglomeratus (Sharp Dock). Seedlings of this species are indistinguishable in shape from *R. sanguineus*. The very rounded apex of the first true leaf separates it from the other *Rumex* species except for *R. obtusifolius*, which differs in the angle at which the blade meets the leaf stalk. A perennial weed of grassland and waste places; common in the British Isles except for Scotland.

Rumex sanguineus (Red-veined Dock). The seedlings of this species are identical in appearance to *R. conglomeratus*. Features distinguishing it from other *Rumex* species are the same as for *R. conglomeratus*. Habitat, distribution and frequency are also similar.

Rumex acetosella (Sheep's Sorrel). The smaller size of the seedling should help to distinguish it from the other *Rumex* species. The only other species with a bluntly-pointed first true leaf is *R. crispus*, which has a more abruptly tapered base to the blade. The fifth and subsequent leaves of *R. acetosella* (illustrated separately) have a characteristic pair of basal lobes. A common perennial weed of arable, grass and heath land; generally on acid sandy soils throughout the British Isles.

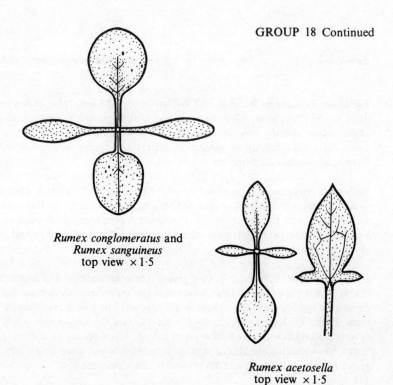

Rumex conglomeratus and
Rumex sanguineus
top view × 1·5

Rumex acetosella
top view × 1·5

Cotyledons as broad as long; first true leaf or pair of leaves entire and hairless.

Epilobium montanum (Broad-leaved Willow-herb). The small size of this seedling and the virtually stalkless first true leaves distinguish it from *Valerianella* and *Rorippa*, and the very rounded tips of the leaves from *E. tetragonum*. A perennial weed common in gardens it occurs throughout the British Isles. Germination takes place mainly in autumn.

Epilobium tetragonum (Square-stemmed Willow-herb). The small size and virtually stalkless first true leaves distinguish this species from *Valerianella* and *Rorippa* and the relatively more pointed leaves from *E. montanum*. A locally common perennial weed of arable and waste land in England and Wales.

Rorippa sylvestris (Creeping Yellow-cress). The long stalks of the leaves, the characteristic shape of the later leaves and the very small cotyledons distinguish this species from the others in this group. There is a resemblance to some forms of *Papaver rhoeas* in Group 17, but the cotyledons are very different. *Rorippa* is often an olive-green colour. It is a perennial, occurring in many non-agricultural habitats, and is sometimes a bad weed in gardens. It grows mainly in England and Wales and is rare elsewhere.

Valerianella locusta (Lamb's Lettuce, Corn Salad). The veined first true leaves, which taper gradually into their broad stalks, should distinguish this species from the rest of the group. An annual weed of arable land and waste places it occurs throughout the British Isles especially on lighter soils. *V. dentata* is similar in appearance, but much less common.

Epilobium montanum
top view ×1·5

Epilobium tetragonum
top view ×1·5

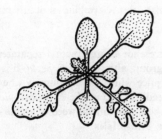

Rorippa sylvestris
top view ×1·5

Valerianella locusta
top view ×1·5

GROUP 20   12 Species

Cotyledons oval to long oval; first true leaves entire and hairless.

Euphorbia helioscopia (Sun Spurge). The small serrations towards the tips of the true leaves and the presence of an epicotyl distinguish this seedling from the others in this group. The other two spurges also have epicotyls. All spurges contain a milky juice which exudes quickly when the stem is broken. The dull blue-green colour is occasionally tinged with purple and the cotyledons are purple beneath. A common annual weed of arable land, waste ground and gardens throughout the British Isles. Germination occurs mainly in late spring and summer.

Euphorbia peplus (Petty Spurge). The presence of an epicotyl separates the spurges from the other seedlings in this group, although in *E. peplus* it is very short. All spurges also contain a milky juice which exudes quickly when the stem is broken. This species has unserrated leaf tips unlike *E. helioscopia* and has broader leaves than *E. exigua*. It is a common annual weed of arable land, gardens and waste places throughout the British Isles.

Euphorbia exigua (Dwarf Spurge). The long epicotyl and the narrow unserrated leaves distinguish this seedling from the rest of the group. Like the other spurges it contains a milky juice. A common weed of arable land occuring mainly in southern and eastern England. It germinates only in spring.

Cardaria draba (Hoary Cress, Thanet Cress, Hoary Pepperwort). The main character of this rather featureless seedling is the very long stalk (up to one and a half times the length of the blade) of the first true leaves. It is generally glabrous but occasionally has a few hairs. A perennial weed of arable land in England and Wales which is spreading rapidly.

Hypericum perforatum (Perforate St. John's Wort). This species is readily identified in the seedling stage by the black dots around the margins of the true leaves. They are most noticeable on very young leaves. A perennial weed of grassland especially on calcareous soils, it occurs throughout most of the British Isles except for the extreme north.

Rumex acetosa (Sorrel). The rounded first true leaf and the pointed basal lobes of the second true leaf distinguish this seedling from the others in this group. At the first true leaf stage it resembles *Rumex obtusifolius* (Group 18) in leaf shape, but *R. acetosa* is smaller and has shorter cotyledons. A common weed of grassland throughout the British Isles.

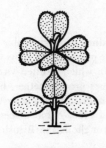

Euphorbia helioscopia
oblique view × 1·5

Euphorbia peplus
oblique view × 1·5

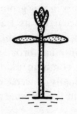

Euphorbia exigua
oblique view × 1·5

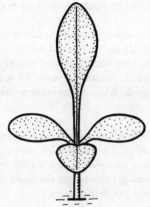

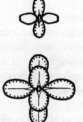

Hypericum perforatum
top view × 1·5

Cardaria draba
oblique view × 1·5

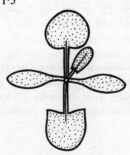

Rumex acetosa
top view × 1·5

Polygonum hydropiper (Water-pepper). A large seedling distinguishable from the others in this group by its long hypocotyl and the purple-black spots which often occur on its leaves. *P. persicaria* (Group 23), which is often virtually hairless, may be confused with it as they sometimes grow together, but *P. hydropiper* has broader cotyledons and a more rounded tip to the first true leaf. A common plant mainly of stream-sides and other damp places, but occasionally a weed of arable land. It occurs throughout the British Isles except in the extreme north.

Chenopodium polyspermum (All-seed). This seedling can be separated from the rest of the group by the broad and virtually stalkless true leaves. The whole plant is usually tinged with purple and the undersurface of cotyledons and true leaves can be bright purple. An annual weed of arable and waste land, locally common in the south and east of England and east Wales.

Thlaspi arvense (Penny Cress). A very characteristic light-green seedling with broad cotyledons often curved downwards at the tip and a long hypocotyl. The first true leaves sometimes have very slightly wavy margins. When bruised the plant has an unpleasant smell. An annual weed of arable land and waste places throughout the British Isles. Germination takes place mainly in spring.

Lychnis flos-cuculi (Ragged Robin). The seedling has narrow cotyledons and leaves which distinguish it from the rest of this group with the exception of *Euphorbia exigua*, which differs in having an epicotyl and a long hypocotyl, and *Chaenorhinum minus*, which has rounded tips to the cotyledons. A common plant of damp grassland throughout the British Isles.

Chaenorhinum minus (Lesser Toadflax). This is a difficult seedling to identify as it has no distinctive characters. It can be separated from the four other small seedlings in this group only by minor differences of leaf shape. An annual weed of arable land and waste places, especially on railway embankments, throughout the British Isles except for the north of Scotland.

Chrysanthemum leucanthemum (Ox-eye Daisy). Up to the two leaf stage this seedling is difficult to identify, but the third and later leaves have very distinctive step-like lobing. It is normally glabrous but may have a very few hairs. A weed of grassland throughout the British Isles.

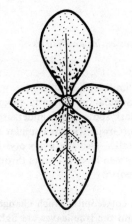

Polygonum hydropiper
top view × 1·5

Chenopodium polyspermum
top view × 1·5

Lychnis flos-cuculi
top view × 1·5

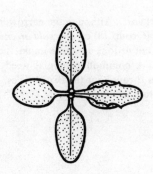

Thlaspi arvense
top view × 1·5

Chrysanthemum leucanthemum
top view × 1·5

Chaenorhinum minus
top view × 1·5

57

Cotyledons sharply pointed; first true leaves entire and hairless.

Anagallis arvensis ssp. arvensis (Scarlet Pimpernel). A shiny dark-green seedling. The cotyledons and leaves are triangular in the early stages and the seedling is further characterized by the dark spots on the undersurface of the true leaves. The leaves of *Stellaria media* (Group 23) are a similar shape, but are light-green and have hairs on the stalks, also the hypocotyl is long. A common annual weed of cultivated and waste land, it occurs throughout the British Isles although more rarely in the north.

Linaria vulgaris (Yellow Toadflax). The cotyledons, which change in shape during development (see illustrations), and the true leaves are light green in colour. The seedling also differs from the other two in having a long hypocotyl and epicotyl. A perennial weed of grassland, cultivated ground and waste places, especially on calcareous soils, throughout most of the British Isles although much less common in Ireland and northern Scotland.

Sagina procumbens (Procumbent Pearlwort). Although the narrow leaves may resemble those of *Scleranthus annuus* (Group 18) or *Spergula arvensis* (Group 13) the seedling is very small and the cotyledons are quite unlike those of any other weed illustrated in this book. A common perennial weed of lawns, gardens, arable land and waste places throughout the British Isles. Germination takes place in spring and late autumn.

Anagallis arvensis ssp. arvensis
top view × 1·5

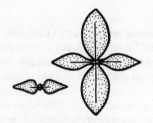

Linaria vulgaris
top view × 1·5

Sagina procumbens
oblique view × 1·5

Cotyledons hairy; first true leaves entire and hairy. (See also Group 28)

Lithospermum arvense (Corn Gromwell, Bastard Alkanet). The long hypo-cotyl and the broad dull-green velvety cotyledons with slightly indented ends make this seedling easily identifiable. An annual weed of arable and waste land mainly on calcareous soils in southern and eastern England.

Anchusa arvensis (Bugloss). The large cotyledons with bluntly pointed tips and the hairs with swollen bases on the true leaves distinguish this seedling from the others in the group. The first leaves, which are blue-green in colour and rough to the touch, tend to be erect while the cotyledons lie flat on the ground. An annual weed of arable and waste land especially on light soils throughout the British Isles except central and western Ireland.

Solanum nigrum (Black Nightshade). The sharply pointed cotyledons separate this seedling from the other three in the group. The leaves are dull dark-green in colour and often tinged bluish-purple. An annual weed of arable land, waste places, market and private gardens, common in England, less common in Wales, rarer elsewhere. Germinates in late spring (May) and summer.

Myosotis arvensis (Field Forget-me-not). The small cotyledons, slightly pointed when young but becoming rounded as they expand, distinguish it easily from the rest of this group. It can be confused with *Bellis perennis* (Group 25), but *Bellis* has no hairs on the cotyledons. *Myosotis* is a common annual weed of arable and waste land throughout the British Isles.

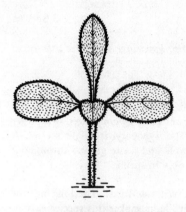

Lithospermum arvense
oblique view × 1·5

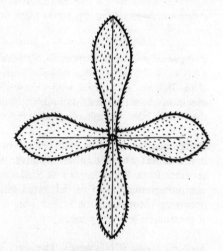

Anchusa arvensis
top view × 1·5

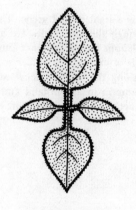

Solanum nigrum
top view × 1·5

Myosotis arvensis
top view × 1·5

Cotyledons oval with a pointed or rounded tip; hypocotyl long; first true leaves entire and hairy or the leaf stalks alone hairy.

Polygonum persicaria (Persicaria, Redshank, Willow Weed). *P. persicaria* has a broad first true leaf with very few hairs, unlike *P. lapathifolium*. It is larger than *Stellaria* and tinged with crimson. The hypocotyl is bright scarlet. A common annual weed of damp soils in arable and waste ground throughout the British Isles. Germination takes place only in spring.

Polygonum lapathifolium (Pale Persicaria, Willow Weed). The long narrow first true leaf which is noticeably silver with hairs makes this species easy to separate from *P. persicaria* and *Stellaria*. The hypocotyl is bright scarlet. A common annual weed of cultivated land and waste places on moist soils occurring throughout the British Isles although less commonly in Scotland. It germinates only in spring.

Stellaria media (Chickweed). The seedling is a light, bright green. The true leaves have long hairs on their stalks although the leaf blades are hairless unlike the two *Polygonum* species. The cotyledons have a lighter coloured tip and a prominent mid-vein. The hypocotyl is often purplish. Older seedlings have a characteristic single line of hairs along the stem. Chickweed is an annual weed that can overwinter; very common in arable land and waste places throughout the British Isles and frequently a serious problem.

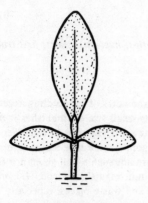

Polygonum persicaria
oblique view × 1·5

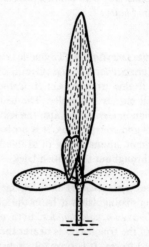

Polygonum lapathifolium
oblique view × 1·5

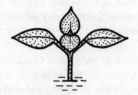

Stellaria media
oblique view × 1·5

Cotyledons oval with pointed or rounded tips; hypocotyl short; first true leaves entire and hairy.

Arenaria serpyllifolia (Thyme-leaved Sandwort). This seedling resembles a miniature *Stellaria media* (Group 23). Its small size distinguishes it from the others in this group except *A. leptoclados* and *Cerastium holosteoides* both of which it closely resembles. The widest point of the true leaves is nearer the base than in *Cerastium*, also the leaves are not such a dull green nor the hairs so erect and conspicuous. It is probably indistinguishable from *A. leptoclados*. A common annual weed of arable land and waste places, especially on light soils, throughout the British Isles.

Arenaria leptoclados (Lesser Thyme-leaved Sandwort). The small size of this seedling distinguishes it from the others in this group except *A. serpyllifolia* and *Cerastium holosteoides*, both of which it closely resembles. The widest point of the true leaves is nearer the base than in *Cerastium* and the few hairs are hard to see. It is probably indistinguishable from *A. serpyllifolia*. Similar to *A. serpyllifolia* in habitats and distribution.

Cerastium holosteoides (= *vulgatum*) (Common Mouse-eared Chickweed). The small size of this seedling distinguishes it from all the others in this group except the two *Arenaria* species. *Cerastium* differs in having the widest point of the true leaves at the middle and the leaves are also a dull dark-green colour with very conspicuous erect hairs. A very common perennial weed of arable land, grassland and waste places throughout the British Isles.

Agrostemma githago (Corn Cockle). The large and stalkless true leaves distinguish *Agrostemma* from all the other seedlings in this group. An annual weed of arable land, it is scattered throughout the British Isles although mainly in southern England. Formerly a very serious weed, but now uncommon.

Hyoscyamus niger (Henbane). The long hairs on the stalks and along the mid-vein of the true leaves are characteristic of this species. The leaf stalks and buds are frequently purple although the leaves themselves are dark-green. An annual weed of waste ground, farmyards, grassland and occasionally arable fields, but scattered and infrequent throughout the British Isles.

Arenaria serpyllifolia
oblique view × 1·5

Arenaria leptoclados
oblique view × 1·5

Cerastium holosteoides
oblique view × 1·5

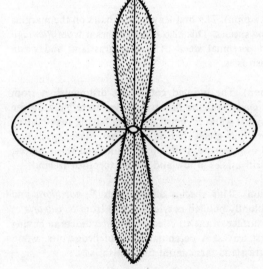

Agrostemma githago
top view × 1·5

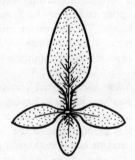

Hyoscyamus niger
top view × 1·5

Plantago media (Hoary Plantain). *Plantago media* has long silvery hairs all over the leaves unlike *Hyoscyamus*, relatively shorter-stalked cotyledons than the *Silene* species and it is smaller than *Agrostemma*. *Plantago major* (Group 18) may also be hairy, but it has long-stalked true leaves. A common perennial weed of calcareous grassland only and confined to England and parts of Wales. Germination occurs in spring.

Silene noctiflora (Night-flowering Catchfly). This seedling differs from the other *Silene* species in having rounded ends to the cotyledons and it has broader cotyledons than *Plantago media*. An annual weed of arable land on light soils mainly in eastern England.

Silene vulgaris (Bladder Campion). The first leaves have hairs on the margins only, unlike the other *Silene* species. This also distinguishes it from *Plantago media*. A locally common perennial weed of arable, grassland and waste places throughout the British Isles.

Silene alba (White Campion). The pointed cotyledons distinguish it from *S. noctiflora* and *Plantago media* and the first true leaves have hairs on the upper surface unlike *S. vulgaris* while *S. dioica* differs in having pointed true leaves. The leaves are more blue-green than in the other *Silene* species. A biennial or perennial weed of grassland, cultivated ground and waste places, common throughout the British Isles in lowland areas except for Ireland.

Silene dioica (Red Campion). This species differs from *S. noctiflora* and *Plantago media* in having bluntly pointed cotyledons and from *S. vulgaris* in having hairs on the upper surface of the true leaves. *S. alba* differs in having less pointed tips to the first leaves. A perennial weed of hedgerows, wood margins and occasionally grassland throughout the British Isles.

Plantago media
top view × 1·5

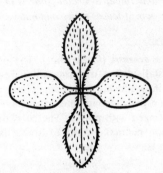

Silene noctiflora
top view × 1·5

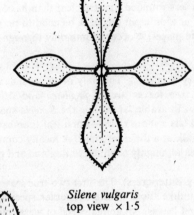

Silene vulgaris
top view × 1·5

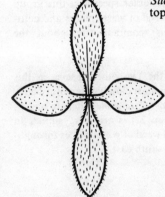

Silene alba
top view × 1·5

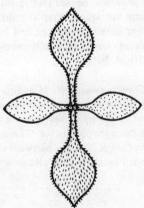

Silene dioica
top view × 1·5

Cotyledons round to ovoid, some with a shallow indent at the apex; first true leaf or pair of leaves entire and hairy.

Mentha arvensis (Corn Mint). The only other seedlings in this group with short-stalked first true leaves are *Senecio jacobaea* and *S. erucifolius*: they differ in producing leaves singly and not in opposite pairs as in *Mentha*, in addition their second true leaves have wavy or indented margins. *Mentha* is often tinged with purple. The hairs on the leaves may be difficult to see. A common perennial weed of arable land and waste places throughout the British Isles.

Senecio jacobaea (Ragwort). *S. erucifolius* and *Mentha* are the only other seedlings in this group with short-stalked first true leaves. *S. jacobaea* differs from *Mentha* in habitat and is only likely to be a problem in neglected grassland. *S. erucifolius* has a less-rounded first true leaf than has *S. jacobaea* and the blade joins the stalk at a different angle. A biennial to perennial weed of poor grassland and waste places, it occurs commonly throughout the British Isles.

Senecio erucifolius (Hoary Ragwort). The only other seedlings in this group with short-stalked first true leaves are *S. jacobaea* and *Mentha arvensis*. *Mentha* is only important in arable land while the *Senecio* species are weeds of grassland. *S. jacobaea* has a more rounded first leaf than has *S. erucifolius* and its blade joins the stalk at a different angle. A locally common perennial weed of calcareous grassland, mainly confined to England and parts of Wales.

Cardamine hirsuta (Hairy Bitter-cress). The first two true leaves of this seedling are kidney-shaped unlike those of the two other species in this group that have long-stalked first leaves. An annual weed of waste places and cultivated land, especially nurseries and gardens: common throughout the British Isles.

Conyza canadensis (Canadian Fleabane). Of the two other species in this group with long-stalked first leaves this seedling most closely resembles *Bellis*, which differs in having more rounded cotyledons. *Cardamine* differs in having kidney-shaped leaves. *Myosotis arvensis* (Group 22) is also very similar in leaf shape, but has hairy cotyledons. An annual weed of waste places throughout England and Wales most commonly in the south-east.

Mentha arvensis
top view × 1·5

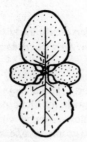

Senecio jacobaea
top view × 1·5

Senecio erucifolius
top view × 1·5

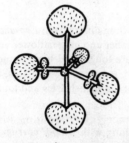

Cardamine hirsuta
top view × 1·5   oblique view × 1·5

Conyza canadensis
top view × 1·5

Bellis perennis
top view × 1·5

Bellis perennis (Daisy). This seedling closely resembles *Conyza*, but is larger and has more rounded cotyledons. *Cardamine* differs in having kidney-shaped leaves. *Myosotis arvensis* (Group 22) is also very similar, but has hairy cotyledons. A very common weed of grassland and lawns throughout the British Isles.

69

Cotyledons oval or rounded, less than three times as long as broad; first true leaf hairy with wavy or shallowly irregular margins.

Lapsana communis (Nipplewort). The distinguishing feature of this seedling is the irregular leaf margin with its blunt points. The young rosettes are completely prostrate and yellow-green in colour, often more yellow than green. An annual weed of waste places and cultivated ground, particularly gardens; occasionally in arable land especially in East Anglia. Common throughout the British Isles.

Sisymbrium officinale (Hedge Mustard). This seedling differs from *Lapsana* in having wavy margins to the leaves. It is much smaller and has shallower veins on the leaves than *Arctium* and the cotyledons are longer and have rounded ends unlike *Legousia*. An annual or biennial weed usually of waste places, but occasionally in arable land. Common throughout the British Isles and locally abundant.

Arctium lappa (Great Burdock). This large seedling with deeply corrugated first true leaves is easily distinguished from the others in this group. A biennial weed of waste places and waysides, it occurs only in the southern half of the British Isles.

Legousia hybrida (Venus's Looking-glass). The seedling differs from the others in this group in having small cotyledons with a definite indent at the tip and first true leaves with two or three pairs of very shallow indents on the margins. An annual weed of arable land on light soils in eastern and southern England.

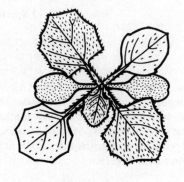

Lapsana communis
top view × 1·5

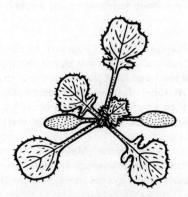

top view × 1·5

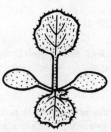

Sisymbrium officinale
oblique view × 1·5

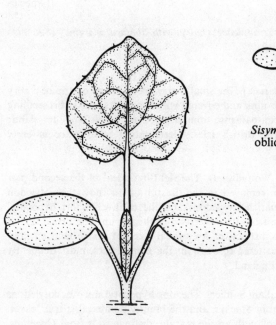

Arctium lappa
oblique view × 1·5

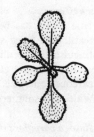

top view × 1·5

Legousia hybrida
oblique view × 1·5

GROUP 27   2 Species

First leaves woolly-hairy and toothed.

Tussilago farfara (Coltsfoot). In the young seedling stage the stalked cotyledons and broader first true leaves distinguish *Tussilago* from *Artemisia*. The second and later leaves are characteristically more angular and not toothed like those of *Artemisia*. A perennial weed of cultivated land and waste places, often a serious problem on heavy land, occurring commonly throughout the British Isles. Germination takes place only in spring.

Artemisia vulgaris (Mugwort). The stalkless cotyledons and narrower first true leaves distinguish *Artemisia* from *Tussilago*. A perennial weed of waste places and waysides throughout the British Isles.

GROUP 28   3 Species

Cotyledons hairy; first true leaves hairy with toothed margins. (See also Group 22)

Odontites verna (Red Bartsia). The small hairy leaves borne on top of a very long hypocotyl, which is pink and covered with long hairs, make this seedling easy to identify. A semi-parasitic annual weed of arable and grassland; common throughout the British Isles. Germination takes place in early spring only.

Stachys arvensis (Field Woundwort). The right-hand leaf of the second pair of true leaves has been removed in the illustration to show the cotyledon beneath. The large squarish cotyledons and the relatively short hypocotyl distinguish this seedling from the other two in this group. The broad tips of the true leaves are also distinctive. An annual weed of arable land on non-calcareous soils, it is scattered throughout the British Isles, most frequently in Wales and southern England.

Galinsoga parviflora (Gallant Soldier). The long hypocotyl and oval cotyledons distinguish *Galinsoga* from *Stachys*, and the bluntly-pointed first true leaves, which have three pairs of teeth on the margin, distinguish it from *Odontites*. An annual weed of arable land (chiefly market gardens) and waste land in and around London; very uncommon elsewhere.

Tussilago farfara
oblique view × 1·5

Artemisia vulgaris
top view × 1·5

Odontites verna
oblique view × 1·5

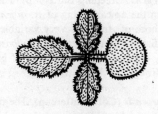

Stachys arvensis
top view × 1·5

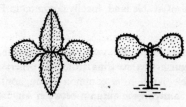

Galinsoga parviflora
top view × 1·5   oblique view × 1·5

Cotyledons glabrous; first true leaves deeply lobed.

Ranunculus acris (Acrid or Meadow Buttercup). The first true leaf of this seedling has lobes all round the margin and not only at the apical end as in *R. arvensis*. It has much larger cotyledons than *Aphanes*. Very variable in leaf shape and hairiness and probably indistinguishable from *R. bulbosus* and *R. repens* in the seedling stage. A very common perennial weed of grassland throughout the British Isles.

Ranunculus bulbosus (Bulbous Buttercup). Lobing of the first leaves is not generally confined to the apical end as in *R. arvensis* and it has much larger cotyledons than *Aphanes*. Very variable in leaf shape and hairiness and probably indistinguishable from *R. acris* and *R. repens* in the seedling stage. A very common perennial weed of grassland throughout the British Isles, but less common in Scotland and Ireland.

Ranunculus repens (Creeping Buttercup). The lobing of the first true leaves is different from the apical lobing of *R. arvensis* and the cotyledons are much larger than those of *Aphanes*. Very variable in leaf shape and hairiness and probably indistinguishable from *R. bulbosus* and *R. acris* in the seedling stage. A very common perennial weed of grassland, waste places and cultivated land throughout the British Isles.

Ranunculus arvensis (Corn Buttercup). The first leaf, which is lobed only near the apex, distinguishes this seedling from the other three *Ranunculus* species. It is very much larger than *Aphanes* and the leaves are less deeply divided. Hairs if present are confined to the leaf margins. The leaves are a light shiny green and the cotyledons often have dark marks near the base (see illustration). An annual weed of arable land, locally common in England but rare in Scotland and Wales.

Aphanes arvensis (Parsley Piert). The very small size and the bright blue-green colour readily distinguish this seedling from the others in this group. An annual weed of arable land, it is common throughout the British Isles. Germination occurs mainly in the autumn between August and October.

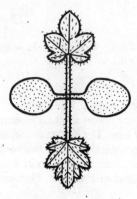

Ranunculus acris
top view × 1·5

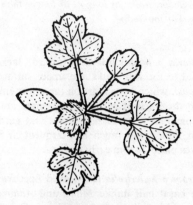

Ranunculus bulbosus
top view × 1·5

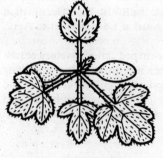

Ranunculus repens
top view × 1·5

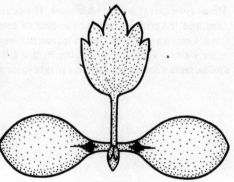

Ranunculus arvensis
top view × 1·5

Aphanes arvensis
top view × 1·5

Cotyledon stalks as long as or longer than the blade; first true leaves hairy and lobed or toothed.

Alliaria petiolata (Garlic Mustard, Jack-by-the-hedge). The hairs are confined to the leaf stalks and under surface of the leaves unlike *Veronica* and *Malva*, which have hairs on the upper surface also. The half-erect cotyledons and the smell of garlic when bruised are also characteristic of this seedling. A biennial weed of hedgerows and gardens, common throughout England and Wales, but much less frequent in Scotland and Ireland. Germination takes place only in early spring.

Veronica hederifolia (Ivy-leaved Speedwell). The leaves are toothed only in the basal half unlike *Malva* and *Alliaria*. In the cotyledon stage it closely resembles *Galium aparine* (Group 5), which also has large dull dark-green cotyledons, but *Galium* differs in having an indent instead of a small knob at the tip. Cotyledons of *Veronica* are often purple on the lower surface. A common annual weed of cultivation throughout the British Isles. Germination takes place through the winter in favourable weather from October to April.

Malva sylvestris (Common Mallow). The pear-shaped and pale-veined cotyledons and the crimson spot at the base of every leaf distinguish this seedling from *Veronica* and *Alliaria*. A perennial weed of waysides, farmyards and other waste places throughout the British Isles, but less frequent in Scotland and Ireland. One of the very few plants to germinate mainly in June and July.

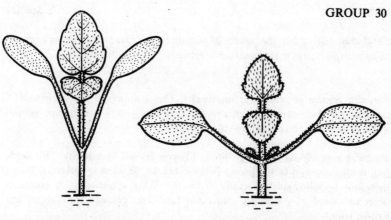

Alliaria petiolata
oblique view × 1·5

Veronica hederifolia
oblique view × 1·5

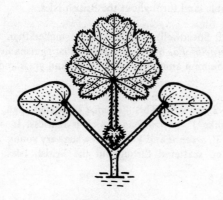

Malva sylvestris
oblique view × 1·5

Cotyledons shaped like the 'spade' of playing cards; first true leaves in opposite pairs with the margins shallowly and regularly notched, usually hairy.

Veronica persica (Buxbaum's Speedwell). The seedling of this speedwell is much larger than any of the other species in this group. A common annual weed of arable land throughout the British Isles.

Veronica serpyllifolia ssp. serpyllifolia (Thyme-leaved Speedwell). This seedling is an exception to the group because the whole plant is glabrous. It can therefore be distinguished easily from the other speedwells. A common perennial weed of grassland, cultivated land and gardens throughout the British Isles.

Veronica agrestis (Field Speedwell). This *Veronica*, which has very variable cotyledons, is smaller than *V. persica* and is hairy unlike *V. serpyllifolia*, but is probably indistinguishable from *V. arvensis* and *V. polita* when very young. An annual weed of arable land throughout the British Isles.

Veronica arvensis (Wall Speedwell). This species is smaller than *V. persica* and hairy unlike *V. serpyllifolia*, but is probably indistinguishable from the other two species. A common annual weed of arable and grassland throughout the British Isles.

Veronica polita (Grey Speedwell). This *Veronica* is smaller than *V. persica* and sparsely hairy unlike *V. serpyllifolia*, which is hairless. It is probably indistinguishable from *V. arvensis* and *V. agrestis* when very young. An annual weed of cultivated land scattered throughout the British Isles, but most common in the south.

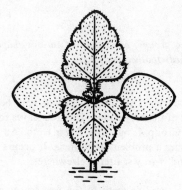

Veronica serpyllifolia
ssp. serpyllifolia
top view × 1·5

Veronica persica
oblique view × 1·5

Veronica arvensis
oblique view × 1·5

Veronica agrestis
top view × 1·5

Veronica polita
top view × 1·5

Species not included in the previous groups; cotyledons of various shapes, first true leaves mostly hairy with variously toothed margins.

Mercurialis annua (Annual Mercury). This large seedling can be easily recognized by the unusual veining of the cotyledons. The true leaves resemble those of the *Galeopsis* species in Group 4, but have fewer teeth. An annual weed of waste places and sometimes a problem in gardens. It occurs mainly in the southern half of England and is very scattered elsewhere.

Senecio vulgaris (Groundsel). The step-like teeth of the first leaves and the narrow cotyledons, which are frequently purple beneath, distinguish this seedling from the other species in this group. Plants can be hairy or glabrous. An annual weed of arable and waste land and frequently a problem: very common throughout the British Isles. Germination can take place during suitable weather throughout the year.

Viola arvensis (Field Pansy). This seedling, which is indistinguishable from *V. tricolor*, is easily identified from the other species in this group by the broadly-rounded apex of the first true leaf and by the oblong dark-green cotyledons. An annual weed of arable and waste land throughout the British Isles.

Viola tricolor ssp. tricolor (Wild Pansy, Heart's-ease). Indistinguishable from *V. arvensis* it is easily identified from the other seedlings in this group by the broadly-rounded apex to the first true leaf and by the oblong dark-green cotyledons. An annual weed of arable and waste land throughout the British Isles, but less common in the south than *V. arvensis*.

Senecio viscosus (Stinking Groundsel). The step-like marginal teeth distinguish this species from the others in this group with the exception of *S. vulgaris*, which differs in having narrower cotyledons. The stems are sticky in older plants and it has a noticeable smell. An annual weed of waste places, scattered throughout England, Wales and Scotland, but locally common.

Chamaenerion angustifolium (Fireweed, Rosebay Willow-herb). This seedling is smaller than the others in this group and the short-stalked true leaves usually have two pairs of very small marginal teeth. The cotyledons are usually a characteristic pear-shape. A perennial weed of cleared woodland, waste places and gardens throughout the British Isles, but much less common in Ireland.

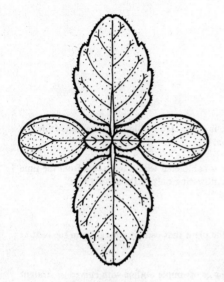

Mercurialis annua
top view ×1·5

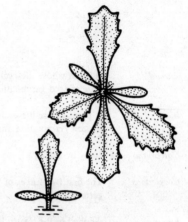

Senecio vulgaris
oblique view ×1·5   top view ×1·5

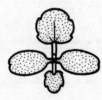

Viola arvensis and
Viola tricolor ssp. tricolor
top view ×1·5

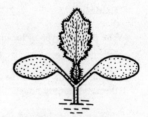

Senecio viscosus
oblique view ×1·5

Chamaenerion angustifolium
top view ×1·5

GLOSSARY

Annual	A plant whose life-cycle is completed within twelve months from the time of seed germination.
Biennial	A plant whose life-cycle is completed within two years from the time of seed germination and flowering only in the second year.
Calcareous	Limy or chalky.
Cotyledons	The first two leaves of the plant that usually emerge from the seed at germination.
Entire	Applied in the text to leaves of simple outline with curved or straight margins (excluding the apex) which are not wavy, toothed, lobed, etc.
Epicotyl	Applied in the text to the length of stalk sometimes present between the cotyledonary node and the node from which the first true leaf arises.
Glabrous	Hairless.
Habitat	The place or type of locality in which a plant grows, e.g. hedgerows, grassland, etc.
Hypocotyl	Applied in the text to the length of stem between the soil surface and the cotyledonary node.
Mealy	Appearing as though covered with meal or flour.
Nodes	The points on a stem from which leaves arise.
Perennial	A plant living for several years and flowering in each year when established.
True leaves	The later leaves of a seedling, developing after the cotyledons.
Whorl	Three or more leaves arising at the same node.

BIBLIOGRAPHY OF ILLUSTRATED
GUIDES TO SEEDLINGS

CHANCELLOR R. J. *Identification of Seedlings of Common Weeds.* Ministry of Agriculture, Fisheries and Food Bulletin 179. H.M.S.O. 1959. (72 pp. in English, illustrated with line drawings.)

DORD D. C. VAN & ZONDERWIJK P. *Kiemplantentabel van Akkeronkruiden.* Plantenziektenkundige Dienst. Wageningen 1961. (60 pp. in Dutch, with line drawings.)

DUNHAM R. S., LARSON A. H. & ROBINSON R. G. *Weed Seedlings.* Minnesota Experiment Station Bulletin 397. (36 pp. in English, illustrated with line drawings.)

FOERSTER E. *Zur Kenntnis der Keimpflanzen einiger Aker- und Grunlandunkräuter.* Rheinische Friedrich Wilhelms-Universitat. Bonn 1957. (91 pp. in German, with line drawings.)

FOGELFORS H. *Weed Seedlings in Sweden.* Uppsala Lantbrukshogskolans 1973. (pp. 233 line drawings and black and white photographs.)

FRASSEN A. M. VAN & WELSENES A. M. VAN. *De Kiemplanten der Tweezaadlobbige Akkeronkruiden* (11) H. Veeman & Zonen. Wageningen 1955. (79 pp. in Dutch, illustrated with line drawings.)

FREDERIKSEN H., GRONTVED P. & PETERSEN H. I. *Ukrudt og Ukrudtsbekaempelse.* Det Kgl. Danske Landhusholdningsselskab. Copenhagen 1950. (320 pp. in Danish, with line drawings.)

GUYOT L. & GUILLEMAT J. *Semences et Plantules des Principales Mauvaises Herbes.* La Maison Rustique, Paris 1962. (94 pp. in French, with line drawings.)

HAAS H. & LAURSEN F. *Weed Seedlings.* Copenhagen. Rhodos 1975. (176 pp. line drawings and black and white photographs.)

HAFLIGER E. & BRUN-HOOL J. (Eds.). *Ciba-Geigy Weed Tables.* Basle, Ciba-Geigy, 1968–1976. (looseleaf folders unpaginated, line drawings.)

HAFLIGER E. & BRUN-HOOL J.(Eds.). *Weed Communities of Europe.* Basle, Ciba-Geigy 1971. (looseleaf, colour photographs.)

HANF M. *Weeds and their Seedlings.* Ipswich BASF UK Ltd. 1972. (348 pp. line drawings and colour photographs.)

IGHE I. & ABERG E. *Ogräs pa akern.* L Ts förlag Stockholm 1962. (99 pp. in Swedish, illustrated with colour photographs.)

KROPAC Z. & NEJEDLA M. *Klicni Rostliny Nasich Beznych Plevelu.* Prague 1956. (pp. 103–241 in Czech, with line illustrations.)

KUMMER A. P. *Weed Seedlings.* The University of Chicago Press. Chicago 1951. (435 pp. in English, with line drawings.)

LÜDERS W. *Unkräuter ungräser.* Landesanstalt fur Pflanzenschutz. Stuttgart 1963. (68 pp. in German, with black and white illustrations and colour photographs.)

MUKULA J. *Rikkaruohot Ja Nüden Torjunta.* Kirjayhtymä, Helsinki 1964. (140 pp. in Finnish, with coloured illustrations.)

PETERSEN H. I. Ukrudtsplanter og Ukrudtsbekaempelse. Det Kgl. Danske Landhusholdningsselskab. Copenhagen 1960. (144 pp. in Danish, with coloured illustrations.)

INDEX

Achillea millefolium 18
Aethusa cynapium 38
Agrostemma githago 64
Alfalfa 6
All-seed 56
Alliaria petiolata 76
Amsinkia intermedia 12
Anagallis arvensis ssp. arvensis 58
Anchusa arvensis 60
Annual Knawel 48
Annual Mercury 80
Annual Nettle 32
Anthemis arvensis 18
Anthemis cotula 18
Anthriscus sylvestris 38
Aphanes arvensis 74
Arabidopsis thaliana 8
Arctium lappa 70
Arenaria leptoclados 64
Arenaria serpyllifolia 64
Artemisia vulgaris 72
Atriplex patula 42

Bastard Alkanet 60
Bellis perennis 69
Bindweed, Field 26
Black Bindweed 44
Black Medick 6
Black Mustard 28
Black Nightshade 60
Bladder Campion 66
Brassica nigra 28
Brassica rapa ssp. campestris 26
Bristly Ox-tongue 8
Bugloss 60
Burdock, Great 70
Buttercup, Acrid 74
Buttercup, Bulbous 74
Buttercup, Corn 74
Buttercup, Creeping 74

Campion, Bladder 66
Campion, Red 66
Campion, White 66
Canadian Fleabane 68
Capsella bursa-pastoris 8
Cardamine hirsuta 68
Cardaria draba 54
Carduus acanthoides 24

Carduus nutans 24
Cat's Ear 40
Cerastium holosteoides 64
Cerastium vulgatum 64
Chaenorhinum minus 56
Chamaenerion angustifolium 80
Chamomile, Corn 18
Chamomile, Wild 20
Charlock 26
Chenopodium album 42
Chenopodium bonus-henricus 42
Chenopodium hybridum 40
Chenopodium polyspermum 56
Chenopodium rubrum 40
Chickweed 62
Chickweed, Common Mouse-eared 64
Chrysanthemum leucanthemum 56
Chrysanthemum segetum 18
Cirsium arvense 22
Cirsium eriophorum 22
Cirsium palustre 22
Cirsium vulgare 24
Cleavers 14
Clover, Red 6
Clover, White 6
Clover, Yellow Suckling 6
Codlins and Cream 32
Coltsfoot 72
Conium maculatum 38
Convolvulus arvensis 26
Conyza canadensis 68
Corn Chamomile 18
Corn Cockle 64
Corn Gromwell 60
Corn Marigold 18
Corn Mint 68
Corn Salad 52
Cornbine 26
Coronopus didymus 46
Coronopus squamatus 18
Cotton Thistle 22
Cow Parsley 38
Cow Parsnip 40
Cranesbill, Cut-leaved 16
Cranesbill, Dove's-foot 16
Cranesbill, Meadow 16
Cranesbill, Small-flowered 16
Creeping Fat Hen 42
Creeping Thistle 22

Creeping Yellow-cress 52
Crepis capillaris 30

Daisy 69
Dandelion 30
Datura stramonium 44
Daucus carota ssp. carota 38
Day Nettle 12
Dead-nettle, Red 10
Dead-nettle, White 10
Dock, Broad-leaved 48
Dock, Curled 48
Dock, Red-veined 50
Dock, Sharp 50

Epilobium hirsutum 32
Epilobium montanum 52
Epilobium tetragonum 52
Erodium cicutarium 12
Erysimum cheiranthoides 8
Euphorbia exigua 54
Euphorbia helioscopia 54
Euphorbia peplus 54

Fat Hen 42
Fat Hen, Creeping 42
Field Madder 14
Fireweed 80
Fluellen 32, 33
Fool's Parsley 38
Forget-me-not, Field 60
Fumaria officinalis 34
Fumitory 34

Galeopsis speciosa 12
Galeopsis tetrahit 12
Galinsoga parviflora 72
Galium aparine 14
Gallant Soldier 72
Garlic Mustard 76
Geranium dissectum 16
Geranium molle 16
Geranium pratense 16
Geranium pusillum 16
Gnaphalium uliginosum 48
Goat's Beard 36
Good King Henry 42
Goosefoot 42
Goosefoot, Red 40
Goosegrass 14
Groundsel 80
Groundsel, Stinking 80

Hairy Bitter-cress 68
Hairy Tare 4
Hawkbit 40
Hawk's-beard, Smooth 30

Hawkweed, Autumn 40
Heart's Ease 80
Hedge Mustard 70
Hemlock 38
Hemp-nettle, Common 12
Hemp-nettle, Large-flowered 12
Henbane 64
Henbit 10
Heracleum sphondylium 40
Herrif 14
Hoary Cress 54
Hoary Pepperwort 54
Hogweed 40
Hop Trefoil, Lesser 6
Hyoscyamus niger 64
Hypericum perforatum 54
Hypochaeris radicata 40

Jack-by-the-hedge 76
Jack-go-to-bed-at-noon 36

Kickxia elatine 32
Kickxia spuria 33
Knotgrass 36

Lamb's Lettuce 52
Lamium album 10
Lamium amplexicaule 10
Lamium purpureum 10
Lapsana communis 70
Lathyrus pratensis 4
Legousia hybrida 70
Leontodon autumnalis 40
Lepidium sativum 12
Linaria vulgaris 58
Lithospermum arvense 60
Lucerne 6
Lychnis flos-cuculi 56

Mallow, Common 76
Malva sylvestris 76
Marsh Cudweed 48
Marsh Thistle 22
Matricaria chamomilla 20
Matricaria matricarioides 20
Matricaria recutita 20
Mayweed, Rayless 20
Mayweed, Scented 20
Mayweed, Scentless 20
Mayweed, Stinking 18
Medicago lupulina 6
Medicago sativa 6
Mentha arvensis 68
Mercurialis annua 80
Milfoil 18
Milk-Thistle, Annual 30

Milk-Thistle, Field   30
Montia perfoliata   36
Mouse-eared Chickweed, Common   64
Mugwort   72
Musk Thistle   24
Mustard, Black   28
Mustard, Garlic   76
Mustard, Hedge   70
Mustard, White   26
Mustard, Wild   26
Mycelis muralis   32
Myosotis arvensis   60

Nettle, Annual   32
Nettle, Perennial   32
Nettle, Stinging   32
Night-flowering Catchfly   66
Nipplewort   70

Odontites verna   72
Onopordum acanthium   22
Orache   42
Oxalis corniculata   6
Oxalis europaea   6
Ox-eye Daisy   56

Pansy, Field   80
Pansy, Wild   80
Papaver argemone-   34
Papaver dubium   46
Papaver lecoqii   46
Papaver rhoeas   46
Parsley Piert   74
Pearlwort, Procumbent   58
Penny Cress   56
Perennial Sow-thistle   30
Perforate St. John's Wort   54
Persicaria   62
Persicaria, Pale   62
Picris echioides   8
Pineapple Weed   20
Plantago lanceolata   36
Plantago major   48
Plantago media   66
Plantain, Great   48
Plantain, Hoary   66
Polygonum aviculare   36
Polygonum convolvulus   44
Polygonum hydropiper   56
Polygonum lapathifolium   62
Polygonum persicaria   62
Poppy, Babington's   46
Poppy, Corn   46
Poppy, Long-headed   46
Poppy, Prickly Long-headed   34

Procumbent Yellow Sorrel   6
Prunella vulgaris   10

Ragged Robin   56
Ragwort   68
Ragwort, Hoary   68
Ranunculus acris   74
Ranunculus arvensis   74
Ranunculus bulbosus   74
Ranunculus repens   74
Raphanus raphanistrum   28
Red Bartsia   72
Red Campion   66
Red Clover   6
Red Dead-nettle   10
Red Goosefoot   40
Redshank   62
Ribwort   36
Rorippa sylvestris   52
Rosebay Willow-herb   80
Rumex acetosa   54
Rumex acetosella   50
Rumex conglomeratus   50
Rumex crispus   48
Rumex obtusifolius   48
Rumex sanguineus   50
Runch   28

Sagina procumbens   58
St. John's Wort, Perforate   54
Scandix pecten-veneris   34
Scarlet Pimpernel   58
Scleranthus annuus   48
Scotch Thistle   22
Self-heal   10
Senecio erucifolius   68
Senecio jacobaea   68
Senecio viscosus   80
Senecio vulgaris   80
Sheep's Sorrel   50
Shepherd's Needle   34
Shepherd's Purse   8
Sherardia arvensis   14
Silene alba   66
Silene dioica   66
Silene noctiflora   66
Silene vulgaris   66
Sinapis alba   26
Sinapis arvensis   26
Sisymbrium officinale   70
Smooth Hawk's-beard   30
Solanum nigrum   60
Sonchus arvensis   30
Sonchus asper   30
Sonchus oleraceus   30
Sorrel   54

Sorrel, Procumbent Yellow 6
Sorrel, Sheep's 50
Sowbane 40
Sow-thistle, Annual 30
Sow-thistle, Perennial 30
Spanish Lettuce 36
Spear Thistle 24
Speedwell, Buxbaum's 78
Speedwell, Field 78
Speedwell, Grey 78
Speedwell, Ivy-leaved 76
Speedwell, Thyme-leaved 78
Speedwell, Wall 78
Spergula arvensis 36
Spurge, Dwarf 54
Spurge, Petty 54
Spurge, Sun 54
Spurrey, Corn 36
Stachys arvensis 72
Stellaria media 62
Stinging Nettle 32
Stinking Groundsel 80
Stinking Mayweed 18
Storksbill, Common 12
Swine-cress 18
Swine-cress, Lesser 46

Taraxacum officinale 30
Tare, Hairy 4
Tare, Smooth 4
Thale Cress 8
Thanet Cress 54
Thistle, Cotton 22
Thistle, Creeping 22
Thistle, Marsh 22
Thistle, Musk 24
Thistle, Scotch 22
Thistle, Spear 24
Thistle, Welted 24
Thistle, Woolly 22
Thlaspi arvense 56
Thorn-apple 44
Thyme-leaved Sandwort 64
Thyme-leaved Sandwort, Lesser 64
Toadflax, Lesser 56
Toadflax, Yellow 58
Tragopogon pratensis 36
Treacle Mustard 8
Trifolium dubium 6
Trifolium pratense 6

Trifolium repens 6
Tripleurospermum maritimum ssp. inodorum 20
Tussilago farfara 72

Urtica dioica 32
Urtica urens 32

Valerianella dentata 52
Valerianella locusta 52
Venus's Comb 34
Venus's Looking-glass 70
Veronica agrestis 78
Veronica arvensis 78
Veronica hederifolia 76
Veronica persica 78
Veronica polita 78
Veronica serpyllifolia ssp. serpyllifolia 78
Vetch, Common 4
Vetchling, Meadow 4
Vicia hirsuta 4
Vicia sativa 4
Vicia tetrasperma 4
Viola arvensis 80
Viola tricolor ssp. tricolor 80

Wall Cress 8
Wall Lettuce 32
Water-pepper 56
Welted Thistle 24
White Campion 66
White Clover 6
White Dead-nettle 10
White Mustard 26
Wild Carrot 38
Wild Chamomile 20
Wild Radish 28
Wild Turnip 26
Willow Weed 62
Willow-herb, Broad-leaved 52
Willow-herb, Great Hairy 32
Willow-herb, Rosebay 80
Willow-herb, Square-stemmed 52
Woolly Thistle 22
Woundwort, Field 72

Yarrow 18
Yellow Suckling Clover 6
Yellow Toadflax 58
Yellow-cress, Creeping 52